OFFSET PLATEMAKING

Deep-Etch

by
Robert F. Reed

Issued by
Lithographic Technical Foundation, Inc.
131 East 39th Street   New York 16, N. Y.

Lithographic Technical Foundation, Inc.
131 East 39th•Street   New York 16, N. Y.

TABLE OF CONTENTS

FOREWORD

This book is designed as an elementary text for beginners in offset platemaking. Its main purpose is to teach the best methods of making *deep-etch plates on zinc and aluminum,* the metals most commonly used by the trade. Use of the least important metal, stainless steel, will be covered briefly. And, since one type of bimetal plate is made in much the same way as a deep-etch plate, a chapter will be devoted to this subject.

This text should give the beginner a thorough understanding of the principles of the deep-etch process and the correct methods of carrying out the various steps in making deep-etch plates. It should help him avoid the many pitfalls he would encounter in learning without adequate guidance.

The following books on deep-etch platemaking have also been published by LTF. They are designed primarily for skilled platemakers and pressmen who want to know the best methods and techniques in preparing deep-etch plates and in getting the best results from them on the press.

No. 804, "How to Make and Run Deep-Etch Plates — Grained Zinc."

No. 804S, "How to Make Deep-Etch Plates on Ungrained Zinc and Aluminum."

No. 806, "How to Make and Run Deep-Etch Plates — Grained Aluminum."

INTRODUCTION

LITHOGRAPHIC PRINTING SURFACES

Lithography is the process of printing from surfaces that are essentially flat. Lithographic printing plates have their image and non-image areas on the same level. A cross section of a plate, if enlarged, would look like Figure 1. The image areas are also called "work areas" or "printing areas". They are not raised as in type or letterpress plates (Figure 2), or depressed as in gravure printing surfaces (Figure 3).

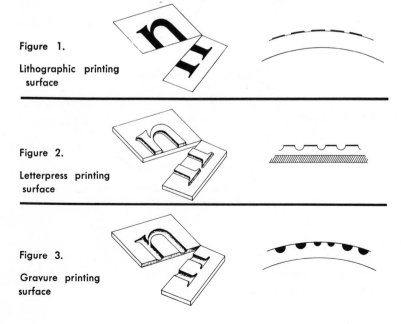

Figure 1.

Lithographic printing surface

Figure 2.

Letterpress printing surface

Figure 3.

Gravure printing surface

Since lithographic ink is applied to the printing areas by means of rollers, the non-printing areas must be prevented from taking ink from the rollers. This is done by keeping these areas moistened with water. So the lithographic press has both dampening rollers and inking rollers. Lithographic platemaking is therefore the process of forming an image or design on a metal plate that will take greasy ink, and then treating the non-image areas so they will take water and, when moist, will refuse ink.

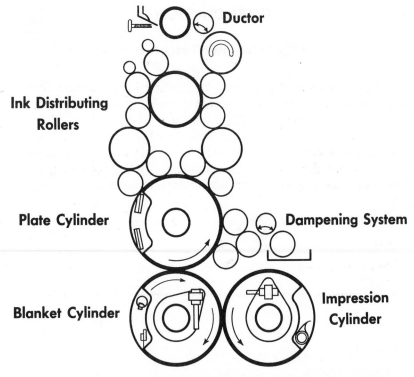

Figure 4. Cross-sectional diagram showing the positions of dampening and inking rollers relative to the plate cylinder of an offset press.

TYPES OF LITHOGRAPHIC PLATES

There are a number of ways to put the ink-receptive design on a lithographic plate, and plates made by the different methods are named accordingly.

Original Plates

These are plates on which the artist first draws a design with greasy crayon or a special ink called tusche. He can also apply a mechanical dot pattern, called Ben Day, with a greasy ink. After the design is finished, the non-design areas are desensitized (made water-receptive and ink-rejecting). This is done by treating them with a "desensitizing etch" which is a solution containing a gum, an acid, and usually one or two salts. It is not an ordinary etch since it removes practically no metal from the plate surface. What it does is to leave an invisible film of gum on the non-image areas which makes them easily wet by water. The gum film also prevents ink from sticking to these areas. After being thus desensitized, the plate is put on a press and printed by the lithographic process of first dampening, then inking, then transferring the ink to paper.

Hand-Transfer Plates

Where two or more identical designs must be printed from the same plate, the artist doesn't draw the same design two or more times. This would be expensive and the designs wouldn't be identical. Instead, he draws a single design from which the required number of ink impressions are pulled on hand-transfer paper. This is a special paper coated on one side with a gummy or gelatinous layer. The duplicate transfers are laid face down in the proper positions on a new plate, and their ink images are pressed against the plate with heavy pressure. Afterwards, the transfer paper is soaked with water and peeled off, leaving the ink images on the plate. Finally, the non-image areas are desensitized and the hand-transfer plate is ready for the press.

Photolithographic Plates

Original and hand-transfer plates are seldom used today. They have almost entirely been replaced by printing plates made photographically from negatives or positives. To make a photolithographic plate, a metal plate must first be coated with a film of light-sensitive material. This is a material that is soluble in water but becomes insoluble when it is exposed to light. A negative or positive of a design on film or glass is then placed in close contact with the coated plate in front of a strong arc light. The light that goes through the transparent parts makes the plate coating insoluble. Where the plate is shaded by the opaque parts, the coating remains soluble. After this light exposure the plate is developed to make the image (design) areas ink receptive, and desensitized to make the non-image areas water receptive.

The reason why photolithographic plates have replaced original and hand-transfer plates is two-fold; (1) they take much less time to make and cost less, and (2) their quality is much better.

There are several kinds of photolithographic plates. We will give a brief description of each to show how they are different.

ALBUMIN OR SURFACE PLATES. The light-sensitive coating for surface plates is a mixture of egg albumin, casein or soybean protein, and ammonium bichromate. (For information about these materials, see LTF Bulletin No. 401, "The Chemistry of Lithography.") To make a surface plate you (1) apply this coating to a metal plate, (2) expose the coating to light through a *negative,* (3) apply a film of greasy ink to the exposed coating, (4) develop the plate in water to *dissolve the unhardened coating off the non-image areas,* and (5) apply a plate etch to desensitize the non-image areas. The hardened parts of the coating with their film of ink stay on the plate and act as the printing areas.

Figure 5. Cross section of a surface plate.

Another kind of surface plate is the "pre-sensitized" plate developed since World War II. These plates are so-called because they are already sensitized when purchased and will keep for six months to a year. Pre-sensitized plates are aluminum plates, usually ungrained, that have been coated with a film of a light-sensitive material called "diazo" compound. So all the platemaker has to do is expose the plate through a negative and develop it with a special developer. It is then ready for the press.

In 1953, about 70 per cent of all lithographic plates made in the United States were surface plates.

DEEP-ETCH PLATES. The light-sensitive coating for deep-etch plates is a mixture of gum arabic and ammonium bichromate. To make a deep-etch plate you (1) apply this coating to a zinc, aluminum or stainless steel plate, (2) expose the coating to light through a *positive,* (3) develop the plate with a special solution to *dissolve the unhardened coating from the image areas,* (4) use a special acid solution to etch away a little metal from the image areas, and (5) apply a special lacquer and ink to the image areas. After this you (6) soak the gum stencil in water to soften it, then scrub it off the non-image areas and (7) apply a plate etch to desensitize these areas.

In 1953, about 25 per cent of all lithographic plates were deep-etch plates.

BIMETAL PLATES. All of the plates previously mentioned are single-metal plates—zinc, aluminum or stainless steel. Bimetal plates are different. They are plates of two metals, one of which forms the image areas and the other the non-image areas. The metal forming the image areas is selected for its ability to take ink, and the metal forming the non-image areas is selected for the ease with which it takes water and can be desensitized to ink. There are several types of bimetal plates in use, but all except one have copper for their image areas because copper is easily made and kept ink receptive. Aluminum, stainless steel and chromium are the metals chosen for the non-image areas because these metals normally accept water in preference to greasy ink. When copper and chromium are used together, they are usually electroplated as layers on zinc or steel plates. Such plates are often called trimetal or polymetal plates even though the third or base plate metal takes no part in the formation or printing of the image. Two general platemaking methods are used. One is like the method for making surface plates. The other is like the deep-etch platemaking process.

Chapter 1

DEEP-ETCH PLATES AND THEIR PURPOSE

Deep-etch plates are so-called because their image areas are etched slightly below the level of their non-image areas. The term "deep-etch", however, gives somewhat of a wrong impression. The etching of the image areas is not deep, but very shallow. Actually, the average depth of etching is not over two to three ten-thousandths of an inch (.0002 to .0003 inch). These figures are from laboratory measurements. The plate-maker doesn't measure the etching depth on his plates because this requires an expensive microscope and takes time. But he can control the etching depth by carefully controlling the time he allows his deep-etching solution to act on the image areas.

Figure 6. Cross section of a deep-etch plate.

Deep-etch plates are considered more durable than surface plates for two reasons:

1. The deep-etched image areas, being slightly recessed, are not affected as much by the abrasive action of dampening rollers, ink rollers and the offset blanket during printing.

2. There is no light-hardened coating left on the deep-etched image areas. Instead, there is a thin film of tough, moisture-resistant lacquer to which the ink adheres. On surface plates

6

the light-hardened coating remains on the image areas and is the base or foundation to which the ink or lacquer adheres. This light-hardened coating, while very thin and tough, is more easily damaged in printing than the lacquer on the deep-etched image.

Besides better durability, deep-etch plates have several other advantages over surface plates:

3. Deep-etch plates are made from positives, and tone values on positives are easier to judge and control than on negatives.

4. The tone values on a deep-etch plate can be controlled in the developing step. The platemaker can thus vary the tone values on the plate to some extent to compensate for deficiencies in positives or incorrect exposures.

5. Deep-etch plates are easier to desensitize than surface plates. This makes it possible to use finer plate grains which require less moisture in printing and yield better quality halftones.

Before about 1930 lithographers had only one type of photolithographic plate, the albumin plate. This was, of course, a surface plate made with a bichromated albumin light-sensitive coating. The average printing life of these plates was fairly short, the maximum being about 50,000 impressions. But they lacked dependability and many failed at 5,000 or 10,000 impressions. It was this situation that made lithographers look for a better plate, and deep-etch plates were developed to supply this need. They proved to be suprior from the start. Maximum printing life was practically doubled, and there was a great improvement in dependability, but there were also many failures and headaches.

Since 1930 a great deal of research has been done to improve both surface and deep-etch plates. Its success is shown by the fact that both types of plates are now used for press runs of from 100,000 to 200,000. However, lithographers generally feel that deep-etch plates are more dependable than surface plates, and that their printing quality holds up better in long runs. Deep-etch plates have been known to run over a million impressions.

The desire for plates that would be highly dependable for runs over 200,000 led to the development of bimetal plates in the late 1930's. Their general use was delayed until after World War II, but their value has been proved and their use is now extensive and increasing. Their maximum press life hasn't yet been established, but it runs into the millions. But, because their printing quality and life is so dependable, many lithographers use them for relatively short runs. One type of bimetal plate is very much like a deep-etch plate, and is made by essentially the same process.

Surface plates are the cheapest to make and they are used for the great majority of the shorter runs. The cost of deep-etch plates is higher, and that of bimetal plates the highest. The cost of bimetal plates is high because of the expensive operations of copper and chromium plating required to make them. The kind of plate chosen by a lithographer, therefore, depends on the nature of his work. If he has fairly long runs, or medium-length runs of high quality work, he generally chooses deep-etch plates.

Chapter 2

MEASUREMENTS IN PLATEMAKING

The lithographic platemaker must make various kinds of measurements. If he prepares his own platemaking solutions, he will have to weigh out definite amounts of solid materials and dissolve them in measured volumes of water or other liquids. Even if he uses commercially prepared solutions, he will sometimes have to adjust their strength, and this will require measurements by weight or volume.

The platemaker must also be able to make measurements of temperature, specific gravity or Baumé, pH (acidity or alkalinity), and relative humidity. These are the main things that determine whether platemaking solutions will or will not work properly. If any of them vary, the quality of the finished plates will vary. Therefore, the only way a platemaker can produce uniformly good plates is to use measurements as controls to prevent variations.

There are, of course, many shops in which temperature and relative humidity can't be controlled or kept constant. In such shops it becomes necessary to make changes in the platemaking process or in the strength of solutions to compensate for changes in temperature or relative humidity or both. These changes have been worked out carefully by research.

Accurate measurement and control at every step is the key to production of uniformly good plates. And uniformly good plates are necessary to efficient press production. Any plate that causes trouble on the press or has to be made over means a loss of profit on the job. Hit-and-miss methods just won't do in the modern shop. So this chapter will be devoted to measurements, how to make them, and how they can help the platemaker.

WEIGHT

All solid or dry chemicals are measured by weight, and the measuring instrument is the scale or balance. Scales vary in capacity and precision depending on the quantities of materials to be weighed on them.

Two systems of weights are used in the United States. The U.S. System of pounds and ounces is the one most commonly used in trade. The Metric System of kilograms and grams is universally used in laboratories, but is also being used more and more in the sale of chemicals. The relationship of the two systems is shown in the following table:

UNITS OF WEIGHT

U. S. System

16 avoirdupois ounces (avoir. oz.)=1 pound (lb.)

Metric System

1000 grams (g.)=1 kilogram (kg.)
1000 milligrams (mg.)=1 gram (g.)

CONVERSION FACTORS

1 avoir. oz.=28.35 g.
1 lb.=453.6 g.
1 kg.=2.2046 lb.
1 kg.=35.27 avoir. oz.
1 g.=.0022 lb.
1 g.=.0353 avoir. oz.

Balances or scales used by lithographers in weighing chemicals for platemaking solutions must be sensitive. A balance using U.S. weights should be sensitive to 1 grain ($\frac{1}{7000}$ lb.). A balance using Metric weights should be sensitive to 0.1 gram.

In LTF bulletins all formulas are given in both U.S. and Metric systems. There are three reasons for this: (1) the Metric system is used exclusively in many foreign countries; (2) the Metric system is more convenient when small quantities are being weighed; and (3) the Metric system simplifies the calculation when larger or smaller quantities are desired than those given in the formula.

Figure 7. Typical balance used for weighing lithographic chemicals.

VOLUME

Water and many other liquids are commonly measured by volume. For this purpose glass "graduates" are used. These are glass vessels, either cone-shaped or cylindrical, that are graduated or marked at various levels to indicate the volumes of liquid they will hold when filled to these levels. Where very small volumes of liquid are wanted, pipettes can be used for greater accuracy. These are tubes into which the liquid can be sucked up to a mark that indicates the desired volume.

Both the U.S. and Metric systems of volume measurements are used in the United States. Their relationship is shown by the following table:

UNITS OF VOLUME

U. S. System	Metric System
16 liquid ounces (liq. oz.=1 pint (pt.)	1000 milliliters (ml.)
32 liq. oz.=1 quart (qt.)	or
128 liq. oz.=1 gallon (gal.)	1000 cubic centimeters (cc.)
2 pt.=1 qt.	=1 liter (l.)
4 qt.=1 gal.	

CONVERSION FACTORS

1 liq. oz.=29.57 ml.	1 gal.=3.785 l.
1 liq. oz.=29.57 cc.	1 ml.=.0338 liq. oz.
1 pt.=473 ml. or cc.	1 l.=33.82 liq. oz.
1 qt.=946 ml. or cc.	1 l.=1.0568 qt.
1 gal.=3785 ml. or cc.	1 l.=.2642 gal.

(Countries in the British Commonwealth use the "Imperial" gallon which is 5 quarts or 160 liquid ounces. One Imperial gallon is therefore 1¼ U.S. gallons.)

Figure 8a. Conical and cylindrical graduates for measuring volumes of water and lithographic solutions.

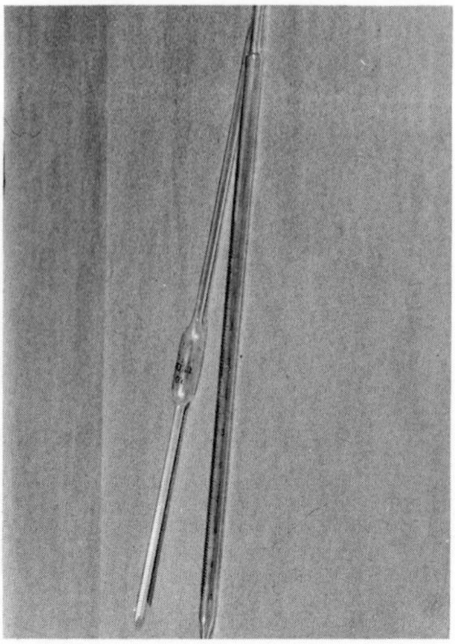

Figure 8b. Plain and graduated pipettes for measuring small volumes of solutions.

For measuring volumes of liquids the cylindrical form of graduate with the levels and figures etched into the glass is always the most accurate. Graduates with the levels and figures molded into the glass are not very dependable.

When you are measuring the volume of a liquid, always read its height to the bottom of its surface as seen through the liquid. Its surface is usually slightly concave and is called the "meniscus".

Since liquids expand when heated and contract when cooled, very accurate measurements of volume must always be made at a specified temperature. But in LTF formulas the temperature is not always specified because all materials are usually at room temperature.

TEMPERATURE

The temperature of a material or substance is its degree of "hotness". You can tell whether a material is hot or cold by feeling it, but if you want to know exactly how hot or cold it is, you have to test it with a thermometer.

Temperature measurement is possible because materials expand when they are heated and contract when cooled. The

Figure 9. Regular mercury and dial-type thermometers.

common mercury thermometer is calibrated in terms of the known expansion of liquid mercury in a tube. Other liquids such as alcohol can be used, and some types of thermometers depend on the difference in expansion of two metals.

Two temperature scales are used in the United States. The one most familiar is the "Fahrenheit" scale (°F.) on which water's freezing point is 32 degrees and its boiling point, 212 degrees. The other is the "Centigrade" scale (°C.) on which water's freezing point is 0 degrees and its boiling point, 100 degrees. To distinguish between them, the temperature figure is always followed by °F. or °C.

Since the difference between the freezing point and boiling point of water is 180° F. or 100° C., it is easy to convert °F. into °C. One Centigrade degree is $\frac{180}{100}$ or $\frac{9}{5}$ Fahrenheit degree. One Fahrenheit degree is $\frac{100}{180}$ or $\frac{5}{9}$ of a Centigrade degree. Thus you can use the following equations to convert one to the other:

(a) $°C. = \frac{5}{9} (°F. - 32)$ (b) $°F. = \frac{9}{5} (°C.) + 32$

EXAMPLE 1:

212° F. is what temperature in °C.?   Using equation (a) we get

$$°C. = \frac{5}{9} (212 - 32) = \frac{5}{9} (180) = 100° C.$$

EXAMPLE 2:

25° C. is what temperature in °F.?   Using equation (b) we get

$$°F. = \frac{9}{5} \times 25 + 32 = 45 + 32 = 77° F.$$

DENSITY

Different liquids have different densities. For example, a liter of water at 4° C. (39 1/5° F.) weighs one kilogram (1000 grams) while a liter of 85% phosphoric acid at the same temperature weighs about 1.7 Kg. Therefore, the density of 85% phosphoric acid is 1.7 times the density of water. We call this figure its "specific gravity".

The most common and handiest instrument for measuring specific gravity or density of liquids is the "hydrometer". This is a weighted glass bulb with a stem in which there is a calibrated scale. The hydrometer is floated in the liquid to be measured. It sinks until the surface of the liquid reaches a certain point on the scale which gives the reading of specific gravity or density.

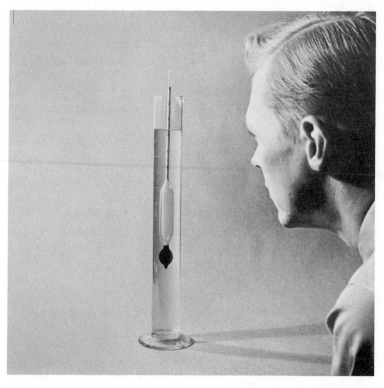

Figure 10. A hydrometer being used to measure the density of a liquid.

Since specific gravity usually involves at least four figures, other simpler hydrometer scales have been devised. The one most commonly used by lithographers is the Baumé scale. On it the density of water at 15.5° C. (60° F.) is 1.0, and density readings require only two, or at most, three figures. For example, a typical gum arabic solution has a specific gravity of 1.1069, but its Baumé density is 14.0. Degrees Baumé is usually written "° Bé."

Actually there are two Baumé scales, one for liquids heavier than water, and another for liquids lighter than water. The latter is used for alcohol solutions and various organic solvents. In lithography, however, we are only concerned with the measurement of liquids or solutions that are heavier than water.

Why are we interested in the density of lithographic platemaking solutions? The reason is that, at any temperature, there is a direct relation between the concentration of dissolved materials and the solution's density. For example, one gallon of an ammonium bichromate solution measuring 14.2° Bé. at 77° F. (25° C.). This is a 20% solution and contains exactly 26¾ avoir. oz. of dry ammonium bichromate (200 grams per liter). If the Baumé is lower than 14.2°, the solution is too weak. If higher, it is too strong. Measuring the Baumé density therefore gives the operator an easy check on his measurements. If he makes a mistake either in a weight or a volume measurement when making up a solution, the final Baumé reading will not be correct.

Baumé hydrometers come in different ranges. A long scale hydrometer will read Baumé degrees from 0 to 100, but it can be read accurately only to 2 degrees. Since lithographic solutions require greater accuracy than this, it is best to use short scale hydrometers. These come in the ranges 0.0 to 10.0, 10.0 to 20.0, etc., and read accurately to 0.1 degree. For deep-etch platemaking solutions the two principal hydrometers you will need are the ones reading from 10.0 to 20.0 and from 40.0 to 50.0.

ACIDITY AND ALKALINITY (pH)

Lithographic platemaking is a chemical process. The results you get depend on chemical reactions between your solutions and the metal plates, and on the chemical changes in the plate coating when it is exposed to light. The main things that control these reactions so you can produce uniformly good plates are:

Temperature

Baumé (density or concentration of solutions)

pH (acidity or alkalinity of solutions)

We won't go into the theory of pH measurement here. You will find it adequately discussed in LTF Bulletin No. 401, "Chemistry of Lithography", Chapter 2. It is sufficient to say that the pH scale is from 0 to 14, and that 7 is exactly neutral. Pure, distilled water has a pH value of 7.00. All acid solutions have pH values below 7, and the lower the pH value, the stronger the acidity. All alkaline solutions have pH values above 7, and the higher the pH value, the stronger the alkalinity.

In the early days of deep-etch platemaking, pH measurement was unknown in our industry. The only control of acidity and alkalinity was in accurate weights and measures in making up solutions. This did not give enough accuracy, and caused a great deal of uncertainty and variation in plate quality. A great deal of the improvement during the past twenty years has been due to platemakers adopting pH control.

 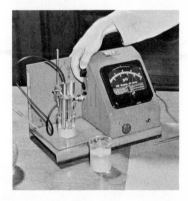

Figure 11a. Slide comparator type of colorimetric pH meter.   Figure 11b. Typical electric pH meter.

The pH value of solutions can be measured by colorimetric and electrometric methods. For a full discussion of these, see LTF Bulletins No. 401, "Chemistry of Lithography" and No.

803, "pH, What it is, How to Measure it, Where to Use it." Of these two methods, the electrometric method, using an electrically operated pH meter and glass electrode, is the more accurate and dependable. It doesn't require color judgment or comparison by the operator. It can measure cloudy or colored solutions. However, continued successful use requires cleanliness and reasonably careful handling of the meter and the buffer solutions used to standardize its readings.

RELATIVE HUMIDITY

Relative humidity is the degree of "dampness" of the atmosphere. It has an important effect on many of the things used by lithographers.

On days when the relative humidity is high, the atmosphere gives some of its moisture to paper and causes it to stretch. On dry days the atmosphere takes moisture from paper and causes it to shrink.

The deep-etch platemaker is interested in relative humidity because the dampness of the atmosphere controls the amount of moisture in the light-sensitive deep-etch plate coating. And any change in the coating's moisture content changes its light sensitivity, that is, the amount of hardening of the coating during any given light exposure. On humid days, plate coatings require less light exposure than on dry days.

One way to prevent troubles due to changing relative humidity is to air-condition the shop. Air conditioning keeps the relative humidity always the same, within narrow limits, regardless of the weather. But this requires expensive equipment and only the larger shops can afford it*. Without air conditioning the platemaker must make certain adjustments according to the prevailing humidity. For example, he must give longer exposures at low humidities, and shorter exposures at high humidities. The relative humidity also affects some other operations in platemaking. So it is necessary for the platemaker to know how to measure relative humidity in order to be guided by it.

Instruments for measuring relative humidity are called "hygrometers". There are several types, but we will describe

*For information on air conditioning in lithographic plants, see LTF Bulletin No. 309 "What the Lithographer Should Know about Air Conditioning."

only those that are practical for the lithographer to use.

The most common form of hygrometer is called a *wet-and-dry-bulb hygrometer*. It consists of two matched thermometers. One of these has its bulb surrounded by a cotton or rayon wick and is called the wet-bulb thermometer. The other is called the dry-bulb thermometer.

To use the wet-and-dry-bulb hygrometer, you moisten the wick on the wet-bulb thermometer with water. Then you place it in a strong current of air, or fan it vigorously, until the temperature shown by the wet-bulb thermometer is as low as it will go. Finally, read both thermometers. Subtract the wet-bulb reading from the dry-bulb reading to find the wet-bulb depression, and consult the table that comes with the hygrometer to find the relative humidity.

The cooling effect on the wet-bulb thermometer is due to evaporation of moisture from the wick surrounding it. The lower the relative humidity of the atmosphere, the faster the evaporation, and the lower the wet-bulb temperature will go at any given dry-bulb temperature.

There are three types of wet-and-dry-bulb hygrometers, as follows:

The *conventional type* has the two thermometers side-by-side, and either stands on a shelf or is hung on the wall. The

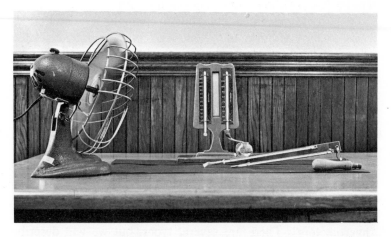

Figure 12. Two types of wet-and-dry-bulb hygrometers. A current of air (note the fan) is needed to produce an accurate relative humidity measurement.

wick from the wet bulb dips in a water fountain, so that it is kept continually moist. Distilled water must be used to prevent the wick from becoming fouled or caked by residues left when the water evaporates. This type of hygrometer will not give correct readings in still air. To get accurate readings you must fan it until the wet-bulb temperature is as low as it will go.

The *sling psychrometer* (means the same as hygrometer) has the two thermometers fastened to a narrow plate that is attached to a handle through a swivel. Each time you use it, you must thoroughly moisten the wick on the wet bulb. Then, holding it by the handle, you whirl the thermometers rapidly for 15 or 20 seconds. Then stop and read the wet-bulb temperature. Repeat the whirling several times until the wet-bulb temperature is as low as it will go. Read both thermometers, then subtract to find the wet-bulb depression, and consult the table to find the relative humidity.

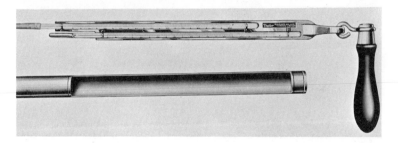

Figure 13. This is a sling psychrometer (hygrometer). After moistening the wick it is whirled to produce the necessary air motion.

The sling psychrometer is the most accurate hygrometer you can use. Its thermometers are usually more accurate than those of conventional hygrometers. And the fact that you have to whirl it, insures sufficient air motion past the wet bulb to give accurate readings.

The *recording wet-and-dry-bulb hygrometer* operates on the same principle as the hygrometers we have just described. But its thermometers actuate pens that trace a record of their readings on a chart. The chart is revolved by clockwork, so that you get a complete 24-hour record. A new chart is installed each day or each week. To find the relative humidity at any time, you simply read the temperatures from the chart, subtract, and consult the humidity table.

The wet bulb of the recording instrument carries a wick that dips into a water fountain. It is enclosed in a tube through which a stream of air is constantly drawn by a small electric fan.

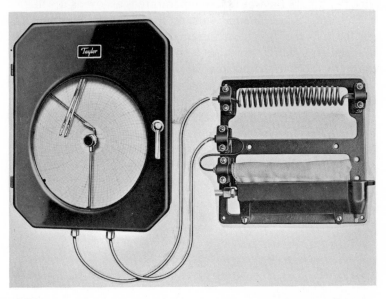

Figure 14. Recording wet-and-dry-bulb hygrometer. In use the wet bulb (lower right) is enclosed, and a fan (not shown) sucks air past it rapidly to assure correct readings.

Recording wet-and-dry-bulb hygrometers are very helpful in a lithographic shop. They eliminate most of the possible human errors and the need for keeping written records. The record of date, time, and humidity makes it easy to check the conditions under which a particular plate was made, and eliminates guessing as to what might have caused good or bad plate performance.

The other form of hygrometer used in many shops depends for its readings on a moisture-sensitive element that expands as the humidity rises and contracts as it falls. One of these is the *hair hygrometer* in which the moisture-sensitive element is human hair. Other forms use either "gold-beater's skin" (membrane from the intestines of cattle) or parchmentized paper.

One very important precaution is, *never add water to strong sulfuric acid*. A lot of heat is generated—enough to cause an explosion and throw acid in your face and over your body. Always add the sulfuric acid carefully to the water solution, in this case the water containing the ammonium bichromate.

Brunak Solution for Aluminum Plates

	Metric Units	U. S. Units
Ammonium Bichromate [$(NH_4)_2Cr_2O_7$]	1350 g.	45 avoir. oz.
Water	20 liters	5 gallons
Hydrofluoric Acid (HF), 48%	160 cc.	5 liq. oz. (150 cc.)

The purpose of the Brunak solution is to make aluminum plates resistant to oxidation. As in the case of the Cronak treatment for zinc plates, the chemistry of the Brunak film formation is not well understood. But it has been proved to prevent the "ink-dot" or oxidation scum that is sometimes troublesome on aluminum plates.

The fumes from *strong hydrofluoric acid* are poisonous and care should be taken not to breathe them. In the Brunak solution, however, the hydrofluoric acid is so weak that there are practically no fumes, and no special precautions are necessary.

Hydrofluoric acid attacks glass, porcelain, and stoneware, and is therefore shipped in wax or polyethylene plastic bottles. If you make up some Brunak solution and use it right away, you can prepare it in a glass bottle. But if you want to keep the solution for any length of time, put it in one-gallon polyethylene bottles.

Ammonium bichromate and the precautions to be taken in handling it have been discussed under the heading "Cronak Solution", page 23.

Deep-Etch Coating Solution

	Metric Units	U. S. Units
Gum Arabic Solution, 14° Bé	720 cc.	3 quarts
Ammonium Bichromate [$(NH_4)_2Cr_2O_7$] Stock Solution	240 cc.	1 quart
Ammonium Hydroxide, 28% NH_3	36 cc.	4¾ liq. oz. (140 cc.)

This is the solution used to coat the counter-etched, Cronaked or Brunaked plate so as to produce a light-sensitive film on it. When exposed to an arc light, this bichromated gum arabic film becomes hardened and insoluble in the deep-etch developer. The parts protected from light remain soluble and are dissolved away.

Gum arabic is a natural gum that comes from Acacia trees in the Middle East and North Africa. Clean gum arabic is an edible product used extensively in candies. It comes in lumps or powdered. The type preferred by lithographers is called *Select Gum Arabic Sorts*. There is no known hazard in its use.

The hazards in handling *ammonium bichromate* were described in connection with Cronak solution (see page 23). A 20% stock solution of it is used for the sake of convenience. The formula is as follows:

Ammonium Bichromate Stock Solution

	Metric Units	U. S. Units
Ammonium Bichromate [(NH$_4$)$_2$Cr$_2$O$_7$], Photo Grade	200 g.	26¾ avoir. oz. (758 g.)
Water to make	1000 cc.	1 gallon

"Water to make" means the final volume after the bichromate has been dissolved.

Ammonium hydroxide is a solution of the gas NH_3 in water. When the 28% solution is exposed to air, some of the gas escapes. It has a strong, sharp odor. Ammonium hydroxide is poisonous if taken into the stomach, but its odor and taste are such that this couldn't be done accidentally. Ammonia vapor in the air has such a strong odor that dangerous amounts cannot be breathed without a lot of discomfort.

The deep-etch coating solution must have its Baumé and alkalinity (pH value) carefully controlled to give uniformly good deep-etch plates. The Baumé affects the coating's thickness on the plate, and pH value affects its light sensitivity and keeping qualities.

LTF Stopping-Out Shellac

	Metric Units	U. S. Units
Orange Shellac	250 g.	8 avoir. oz. (227 g.)
Denatured Alcohol, Water-Free	1000 cc.	1 quart
Methyl Violet Dye	2 g.	⅟₁₆ avoir. oz. (2 g.)

Most natural gums and resins are of vegetable origin and are obtained from trees or shrubs. *Shellac* is different. It is the excretion of the Lac insect. Most of it comes from India. Unlike most vegetable gums, it dissolves completely in alcohol. It is not poisonous and has no ill effects on the skin.

Denatured alcohol is made from ethyl alcohol (grain alcohol or ethanol C_2H_5OH), by adding certain things to it to make it objectionable for drinking. This is done to avoid the high alcohol tax so that alcohol can be used for various commercial purposes.

Completely denatured alcohol contains about five per cent of isopropyl alcohol (C_3H_7OH) plus one or more very bad tasting materials and five to ten per cent of water. It is suitable for radiator antifreeze and can be bought by anyone.

There are a number of specially denatured alcohols used in chemical manufacture, but these can be bought only by registered firms and must be strictly accounted for to prevent their being used to make illegal beverages.

In addition, the Government has licensed certain firms to make and sell specially denatured alcohols for use only as lacquer solvents. These alcohols are sold under trade names, such as Ansol M, Solox, Synacol, and Shellacol. Their formula is:

	Gallons or Liters
Ethyl Alcohol	95
Wood Alcohol	5
Methyl Isobutyl Ketone	1
Ethyl Acetate	1
Gasoline	1

These denatured alcohols are water-free (anhydrous) and are the best alcohols for dissolving shellac.

Denatured alcohols are poisonous if taken internally. The wood alcohol they contain affects the nerves and is likely to cause blindness. Otherwise they are safe to handle and have no effect on the skin except to remove natural oils and leave the skin dry.

The denatured alcohols represent a serious fire hazard. Their vapors can form an explosive mixture with air. Care should be taken to keep them, and lacquer that contains them, cool and away from open flames. Smoking should be prohibited in areas where they are stored or used.

Methyl violet dye is a common purple aniline dye that dissolves in alcohol. It has a strong staining effect on the skin but is not harmful.

Deep-Etch Developers

When the deep-etch plate coating is exposed to light in contact with a positive, the bichromated gum is hardened in the non-image areas. The unexposed coating must then be dissolved off the image areas so they can be deep-etched. Water alone can't be used to do this since it also dissolves too much of the light-hardened stencil. So a special developing solution must be used. The same developer can be used for zinc plates, aluminum plates, stainless steel plates, and for bimetal plates made from positives that require the bichromated gum arabic light-sensitive coating.

LTF's Regular Deep-Etch Developer

	Metric Units	U. S. Units
Calcium Chloride Solution, 40-41°		
Baumé	1000 cc.	1 gallon
Lactic Acid, 85%	53 cc.	6¾ liq. oz. (200 cc.)

The *calcium chloride* solution is made by dissolving 9½ pounds of ordinary commercial calcium chloride flakes ($CaCl_2.2H_2O$) in one gallon of water. The solution gets warm while the calcium chloride is dissolving. When it is all dissolved, allow it to cool to room temperature (75° F.) and test its Baumé. Usually it will be too high. So you adjust it to 40°-41° by carefully adding water.

Calcium chloride is made by dissolving limestone in hydrochloric acid. It is not poisonous and has no ill effects on handling except that it leaves the skin dry. It is a good idea to wear rubber gloves when you handle calcium chloride or deep-etch developer.

Lactic acid is a weak acid made by the fermentation of milk sugar. It is not poisonous or harmful.

LTF's Stabilized Deep-Etch Developer is like the regular solution except that it contains *zinc chloride* ($ZnCl_2$) in place of part of the calcium chloride, and a higher proportion of lactic acid. It has the following formula:

Stabilized Deep-Etch Developer

	Metric Units	U. S. Units
Zinc Chloride (ZnCl$_2$), Technical	350 g.	1½ pounds
Calcium Chloride (CaCl$_2$.2H$_2$O)	700 g.	3 pounds
Water	1000 cc.	2 quarts
Lactic Acid, 85%	160 cc.	11½ liq. oz. (340 cc.)

The action of this developer is less affected by temperature than that of the regular developer. Zinc chloride is not a health hazard unless it is taken internally.

Commercial deep-etch developers are like the LTF developers but may contain other salts than calcium and zinc chlorides, and other acids than lactic acid. They work in the same way, however, and none of them are known to be harmful to the user.

Deep-Etching Solutions

The purpose of deep-etching is to etch or dissolve away a small amount of metal from the image areas of the plate after they have been laid bare by the development. So the deep-etching solution must contain a stronger acid than the one in the developer, and one that is suited to the plate metal. And it must also contain a large proportion of a salt like calcium chloride or zinc chloride to keep it from dissolving or penetrating the bichromated gum stencil that protects the non-image areas of the plate.

LTF's Deep-Etching Solution for Zinc Plates

	Metric Units	U. S. Units
Calcium Chloride Solution, 40-41° Bé	1000 cc.	1 gallon
Iron Perchloride (FeCl$_3$), Lumps	25 g.	3¼ avoir. oz. (92 g.)
Hydrochloric Acid (HCl), 37.0-38.5%	20 cc.	2½ liq. oz. (74 cc.)

LTF's Deep-Etching Solution for Aluminum Plates

	Metric Units	U. S. Units
Calcium Chloride Solution, 40-41° Bé	1000 cc.	89 liq. oz.
Zinc Chloride (ZnCl$_2$), Technical	380 g.	35½ avoir. oz.
Iron Perchloride Solution, 50-51° Bé	285 cc.	25¼ liq. oz.
Hydrochloric Acid (HCl), 37.0-38.5%	14 cc.	1¼ liq. oz. (37 cc.)
Cupric Chloride (CuCl$_2$.2H$_2$O)	27 g.	2½ avoir. oz. (70 g.)

This solution can also be used for deep-etching stainless steel plates.

Calcium chloride, zinc chloride, and *hydrochloric* acid have already been discussed under the heading "Deep-Etch Developers", page 28.

Iron perchloride is the common trade name for ferric chloride ($FeCl_3$). It is used extensively by photo-engravers and gravure etchers for etching copper plates and cylinders. It can be bought as solid lumps, crystals, and also as solutions in water of different Baumés from 40 to 46°. The solutions are highly corrosive to metals and must be kept in glass bottles or carboys. In case you can't buy 50° Bé iron perchloride solution, you can easily make it by dissolving the solid lumps in one of the weaker solutions or in water.

Like strong hydrochloric acid, iron perchloride solution should be handled carefully. Avoid contact with the skin, and take care to avoid splashing or spattering. A drop in the eye would be painful and might injure your eyesight.

Cupric chloride is the chemical name for copper chloride ($CuCl_2$). It is sold as blue crystals that contain some water. So the true formula of the commercial product is $CuCl_2.2H_2O$. There is also another copper chloride (Cu_2Cl_2) which is called "cuprous chloride". We use the names cupric and cuprous to distinguish between them. Cupric chloride is used in the aluminum deep-etching solution because it helps penetrate the film of aluminum oxide that is always present on aluminum plates. It also leaves a small amount of black metallic copper on the deep-etched image areas that seems to improve their image-holding properties. For further information on iron and copper compounds and their action on metal plates, see LTF's Bulletin No. 401, "Chemistry of Lithography".

All copper compounds are poisonous if taken internally. But cupric chloride's only effect on the skin is its corrosive action which is somewhat less than that of iron perchloride.

For bimetal plates you use a special etch that corresponds to the deep-etching solutions for zinc and aluminum plates. Its only purpose is to etch through the chromium layer and lay bare the copper layer underneath. It doesn't attack the copper.

LTF has developed a non-fuming chromium etch for bimetal plates, covered by U.S. Patent No. 2,599,914, issued June 10, 1952, to P. J. Hartsuch and C. Wachtel. Its formula is:

Chromium Etch for Bimetal Plates

	Metric Units	U. S. Units
Aluminum Chloride (AlCl$_3$) Solution, 32° Bé	750 cc.	3 quarts
Zinc Chloride (ZnCl$_2$), Technical	630 g.	5¾ lbs.
Phosphoric Acid (H$_3$PO$_4$), 85%	40 cc.	5 liq. oz.

Aluminum chloride is quite corrosive and should be handled with care. Zinc chloride is a poison but is not a hazard unless it is taken internally. Phosphoric acid is a colorless, syrupy liquid. It is quite corrosive and should not be allowed to remain on the skin for any length of time.

There are also several commercial chromium etches that work satisfactorily. These should be handled with the same care as the deep-etching solutions.

Nicohol Solution

	Metric Units	U.S. Units
Cellosolve Solvent	900 cc.	3 quarts
Nitric Acid (HNO$_3$) Conc., Sp. Gr. 1.42	100 cc.	10 liq. oz.

When zinc and aluminum plates are deep-etched, some of the iron perchloride in the deep-etching solution is reduced to metallic iron. This remains as a black deposit on the image areas. Unless it is completely removed, it can prevent good adhesion of lacquer on zinc plates and the copper deposit on aluminum plates. Treatment with Nicohol solution removes this black deposit.

Cellosolve Solvent is ethylene glycol monoethyl ether. When mixing it and the concentrated nitric acid, be sure to pour the acid into the solvent. Do this slowly with constant stirring. Adding the solvent to the acid might cause an explosive reaction and splash the acid on you.

Once the mixture is made, it is relatively harmless. Nitric acid in the Cellosolve Solvent is not nearly as corrosive as the same amount in water solution. It should be applied with a deep-etch pad. If any gets on your hands, wash them with water.

The Copperizing Solution

This solution is for aluminum plates only. Many platemakers feel that a thin deposit of metallic copper on the image areas of aluminum plates improves their image-holding quality and printing life. Unlike the black copper deposit left by LTF's aluminum deep-etching solution, that produced by the copperizing solution is copper colored.

You can buy a prepared solution or make your own.

LTF's Copperizing Solution

	Metric Units	U. S. Units
Isopropyl Alcohol, 99%	1000 cc.	1 quart
Cuprous Chloride (Cu_2Cl_2)	31 g.	1 avoir. oz. (28.3 g.)
Hydrochloric Acid (HCl), 37.0-38.5%	32 cc.	1 liq. oz. (29.6 cc.)

Isopropyl alcohol is similar to ethyl alcohol but evaporates less rapidly. Its formula is C_3H_7OH. It has a stronger odor and is more toxic or poisonous than ethyl alcohol. However, there has never been any case of harm to operators from breathing its vapors in using the copperizing solution. Isopropyl alcohol is an ingredient of most medicinal "rubbing alcohols".

Like the denatured alcohols previously discussed, isopropyl alcohol represents a fire and explosion hazard. It, and the copperizing solution, should be kept in a cool place, and smoking or open flames should be prohibited in areas where they are stored or used.

Cuprous chloride should be handled with the same ordinary care as cupric chloride. It should be kept in a tightly stoppered bottle since it picks up moisture from the atmosphere and tends to become lumpy and hard to dissolve in the isopropyl alcohol.

Washing Alcohols

After the plate image has been deep-etched or copperized, the next step is to wash off the deep-etching or copperizing solution so that the deep-etch lacquer will hold tightly on the image areas. This is done with one of the anhydrous denatured alcohols, Ansol M, Solox, Synacol, or Shellacol. A description of these alcohols was given under the heading "Stopping-Out Shellac and Lacquers", page 26, and need not be repeated here. Note particularly that they represent a serious fire and explosion hazard unless smoking and open flames are prohibited in areas where they are stored and used.

Deep-Etch Lacquers

While greasy ink will hold well on the freshly deep-etched and cleaned image areas of the plate, these areas are less easily damaged during printing if a suitable lacquer is first applied. This lacquer must have three important properties: (1) it must adhere tightly to the metal surface; (2) it must not be dissolved by the oily varnishes in lithographic inks or by cleaning solvents; (3) it must have a strong affinity for ink, and no affinity for water or gum solutions. Deep-etch lacquers usually have a dye added to them to give them color. This helps the operator to see that he has applied them completely and evenly over the image areas of the plate.

The first deep-etch lacquer ever used was probably shellac dissolved in alcohol. Later on, lacquers were made from nitrocellulose (similar to celluloid), Bakelite, and other synthetic resins. But, while these lacquers adhered well to the metal and were not dissolved off by inks or cleaning solvents, they had some affinity for water and gum. On the press the gum arabic the pressman used in plate and fountain etches, and for gumming up, would sometimes displace the ink so that the image areas became blind (failed to print).

Research at the LTF laboratory has resulted in the development of *"non-blinding" deep-etch lacquers* that meet all three requirements. With them it is almost impossible for plates to become blind and their press life and dependability have been greatly improved. The non-blinding lacquers are based on vinyl resins. Their preparation is too complicated for them to be made in the lithographic shop. LTF has therefore given the necessary information to properly equipped suppliers, and most of these can now supply good non-blinding deep-etch lacquers.

So far as is known, there are no health hazards to the operator in applying the non-blinding lacquers. Some of the solvents in them have strong odors but these are harmless in the amounts to which the operator is exposed.

The solvents used in deep-etch lacquers are inflammable, and care should be taken to keep them cool and away from open flames. Smoking should be prohibited in the area where lacquer is applied to plates.

Developing Ink

Deep-etch developing ink is a stiff, non-drying, greasy black ink thinned with solvents so it can be rubbed down to a smooth, even film on the plate. It is applied on top of the lacquer film.

LTF has never published formulas for developing ink for two reasons: (1) they are complicated and lithographers don't have the necessary equipment to make them properly; and (2) there are a number of good deep-etch devloping inks available from suppliers.

The only hazard in the use of developing inks is that due to the solvents used in them. Some platemakers are sensitive to *turpentine,* and inks that contain it may cause a skin rash called dermatitis (see page 24). The other solvents used are less irritant and cause little trouble. Operators can usually avoid skin irritation by being careful to keep developing inks off their hands.

The solvents in developing ink are inflammable but not explosive. However, they will usually not catch fire from an open flame if they are at room temperature (below about 90°).

Asphaltum Solution

Lithographic asphaltum is used to protect the plate image after the developing ink is washed off. Plates are always stored "under asphaltum" since ink tends to dry or harden.

There are a number of commercial asphaltum solutions available from suppliers.

LTF's Asphaltum Solution

	Metric Units	U. S. Units
Powdered Asphaltum or Gilsonite, (turpentine soluble)	175 g.	23 avoir. oz. (650 g.)
Lithotine	1000 cc.	1 gallon

Asphaltum or *gilsonite* is a natural mineral resin. There are a number of types, but the one used by lithographers should be completely soluble in turpentine.

Originally, asphaltum solution was made with turpentine. But because some platemakers are sensitive to turpentine and develop a skin rash, *Lithotine* was developed by LTF to replace it.

Lithotine

	Metric Units	U. S. Units
Pine Oil, Water Free	90 cc.	10 liq. oz. (296 cc.)
Castor Oil, Technical	9 cc.	1 liq. oz. (30 cc.)
Ester Gum, powdered	18 g.	2 avoir. oz. (57 g.)
VM & P Naphtha or Dry Cleaner's Naphtha	1000 cc.	7 pints

This combination is much less irritating to the skin and is not considered a health hazard. It is also used as a solvent for washing ink and asphaltum off of plates. It can be bought ready-prepared from a number of suppliers.

Both turpentine and Lithotine are inflammable but are not serious fire hazards. They will not catch fire from an open flame if they are at ordinary room temperature (below 90° F.).

Phosphate Solution for Zinc Plates

	Metric Units	U. S. Units
Aluminum Sulfate $[Al_2(SO_4)_3 \cdot 18H_2O]$	15.1 g.	2 avoir. oz. (57 g.)
Potassium Nitrate (KNO_3)	11.5 g.	1½ avoir. oz. (42 g.)
Ammonium Phosphate Monobasic		
$(NH_4H_2PO_4)$	21 g.	2¾ avoir. oz. (78 g.)
Water to make	1000 cc.	1 gallon

The phosphate solution is applied to the plate after the deep-etch stencil has been removed. It increases the effectiveness of non-bichromate plate etches in desensitizing the non-image areas but should not be used with etches that contain a bichromate. None of the chemicals in its formula are harmful in any way, and its use requires no special precautions.

Nital Solution for Zinc Plates

	Metric Units	U. S. Units
Ammonium Alum		
$[NH_4Al(SO_4)_2 \cdot 12H_2O]$	30 g.	4 avoir. oz. (113 g.)
Nitric Acid (HNO_3), Conc.,		
Sp. Gr. 1.42	1 cc.	⅛ liq. oz. (3.7 cc.)
Water	1000 cc.	1 gallon

The Nital solution is used in exactly the same way as the phosphate solution. Of its two chemical ingredients, only the nitric acid requires precautions. Concentrated nitric acid can be dangerous if not handled carefully. It is a highly corrosive liquid that can cause burns on contact with the skin. A drop splashed in the eye could damage eyesight. It also gives off very irritating fumes. Great care should be taken to avoid spilling or spattering of this acid.

Plate Etches

Plate etches are used to desensitize the non-image areas of the plate to ink after the image areas have been formed and the hardened deep-etch stencil has been scrubbed off. In the case of zinc plates they are applied after a treatment with Cronak, Phosphate, or Nital solution. Plate etches desensitize by leaving a thin layer of gum on the plate's non-image areas that prevents ink from wetting them or adhering to them if the plate should accidentally become dry during printing.

LTF has done a great deal of research on plate etches and the best formulas we have found are as follows:

Cellulose Gum Plate Etch for Zinc

	Metric Units	U. S. Units
Phosphoric Acid (H_3PO_4), 85%	7.8 cc.	1 liq. oz. (29.5 cc.)
Magnesium Nitrate, Crystals,		
[$Mg(NO_3)_2 \cdot 6H_2O$]	11.3 g.	1½ avoir. oz. (42.5 g.)
Cellulose Gum, Dry	41 g.	5½ avoir. oz. (156 g.)
Water to make	1000 cc.	1 gallon

Gum Arabic Plate Etch for Zinc, Formula No. 1

	Metric Units	U. S. Units
Water	320 cc.	40 liq. oz.
Tannic Acid	20.6 g.	2¾ avoir. oz. (78 g.)
Chrome Alum [$KCr(SO_4)_2 \cdot 12H_2O$]	30 g.	4 avoir. oz. (113 g.)
Phosphoric Acid (H_3PO_4), 85%	21.4 cc.	2¾ liq. oz. (81 cc.)
Gum Arabic Solution, 14° Bé	680 cc.	88 liq. oz.

Gum Arabic Plate Etch for Zinc, Formula No. 2

	Metric Units	U. S. Units
Ammonium Bichromate		
[$(NH_4)_2Cr_2O_7$], Photo Grade	7.5 g.	1 avoir. oz. (28.5 g.)
Gum Arabic Solution, 12-14° Bé	945 cc.	121 liq. oz.
Phosphoric Acid (H_3PO_4), 85%	18.5 cc.	2⅜ liq. oz. (70 cc.)

Plate Etch for Aluminum and Stainless Steel

	Metric Units	U. S. Units
Gum Arabic Solution, 12-14° Bé	1000 cc.	1 gallon
Phosphoric Acid (H_3PO_4), 85%	31 cc.	4 liq. oz. (118 cc.)

You will note that *phosphoric acid* is in all four formulas. All plate etches must be somewhat acid and phosphoric acid is the best acid we know of for this purpose. Strong phosphoric acid is a clear, colorless, syrupy liquid. It is quite corrosive and should not be allowed to remain on the skin for any length of time.

Magnesium nitrate is a white crystalline salt. The $6H_2O$ in its formula simply means that its crystals contain a certain amount of water. Magnesium nitrate is not poisonous or harmful to the skin.

Tannic acid is a tan colored powder. It has no harmful effects on the skin.

Chrome alum is a slightly purplish salt. Unlike bichromates, it doesn't cause dermatitis and presents no hazards in its use.

Ammonium bichromate has already been discussed under the heading "Cronak Solution", page 23. Particular care should be used in handling plate etches that contain bichromate since they are applied by hand. It is almost impossible to keep from getting some of the etch on the hands, and so easy to forget to wash it off. Platemakers who are known to be sensitive to bichromates should avoid etches that contain it and stick to etches that do not. Others should be careful to keep it off their hands. Rubber gloves are a help only if they are washed thoroughly, inside and outside, before each use.

Cellulose gum (carboxymethylcellulose or CMC) is a relatively new water-soluble gum. It comes as a white powder and has no harmful effects. It is manufactured from cellulose fiber in several types for various purposes. In lithographic etches we use the low viscosity* type.

Cellulose gum has a powerful desensitizing action on zinc plates. Properly used it does a better job of desensitizing than gum arabic. And it works best in plate etches that don't contain bichromates. Some shops that use cellulose gum have reported that it has cleared up dermatitis among their platemakers in addition to making better plates.

Cellulose gum can't just be used to replace gum arabic in any etch formula. The formula must be correct for it, and the finished plate etch should test between 2.9 and 3.3 pH. Cellulose gum doesn't work as well as gum arabic in etches for aluminum plates.

Gum arabic has already been discussed under the heading "Deep-Etch Coating Solution", page 25. Etches for zinc plates that contain it should have pH values between 2.0 and 2.5.

---

*Viscosity is the thickness or resistance to flow of liquids. When we speak of "low viscosity" cellulose gum, we mean the type that, when dissolved in water to a given strength solution, flows or pours more freely than the higher-viscosity types.

Chapter 4

LITHOGRAPHIC METAL PLATES

Lithographic plates today are all thin metal sheets. Zinc is used in most shops, but some shops use only aluminum. Stainless steel and bimetal plates are used for special types of work. Plates are the full size of the press cylinder and they must be thin and flexible enough to wrap around the cylinder snugly. The thickness of regular zinc and aluminum "lithoplate" used for deep-etch plates varies with size of the press, from .012 inch for 17" x 22" presses up to .025 inch for 50" x 76" presses. Some of the older presses take plates .030 inch thick.

Uniform thickness of plates is highly important. Plates up to 22" x 34" should not vary more than .001 inch in thickness. For example, a .012 inch plate must not be less than .0115 inch or more than .0125 inch thick in any area. This is called "gage tolerance" and is usually expressed as ± .0005 (plus or minus .0005) inch. For the larger sized plates the gage tolerance is ± .001 inch.

Metal litho plates are made in a rolling mill and are reduced to their final thickness by cold rolling. This makes them harder. They are then carefully inspected to be sure that (1) they meet the required gage tolerance, and (2) at least one side is free from scale, dents or scratches. Manufacturers of litho plates usually indicate the better side of the plate by marking the reverse side, "Use Other Side". Zinc plates are also supplied with the preferred side belt-sanded to a matte finish.

Mostly, the lithographer uses grained plates. This means

38

that the side of the plate to be used in printing has to be roughened or given a "tooth".

Before about 1900, practically all lithography was done from stones on flat-bed presses. But when rotary presses were introduced, thin metal plates had to be substituted for stones. At that time lithographers didn't know very much about de-sensitizing zinc and aluminum plates. They found that, to print clean, the plates had to have a surface grain to help them carry water on the non-image areas. They developed the plate-grain-ing machine consisting of a horizontally rotating tub, or flat rectangular bed with sides. The plates were held down on the bed with clamps and covered with sand, marbles and water.

Figure 15. Modern plate-graining machine in operation. Marbles from the hy-draulic lift at left have just been dumped onto plates on the bed of the machine.

Rotation of the tub caused the marbles to roll around on the sand, roughening the plate surface and producing the grain. This method of plate graining is still in general use. Graining machines have been greatly improved, and new and better abrasives have been developed, but the principle remains the same.

A great deal of research has been done to try to develop better and faster methods of graining lithographic plates. There are now machines that work on the principles of sand blasting and wire brushing, but they are not yet generally accepted by lithographers. Much work has also been done on "chemical graining" or producing the rough surface texture by chemical etching, but this has not been very successful.

Plate graining is done in many of the larger lithographic plants, but the smaller shops generally have their plates grained by trade shops.

After zinc and aluminum plates have been used, and if they are not needed for re-runs, they are regrained to remove the old work and used again. Plates may be used over again as many as eight to ten times. But when they break at the edges that are clamped to the press cylinder, they have to be discarded or cut down in size and used on smaller presses.

A well grained plate has a dull, uniformly matte surface, is free from shiny spots and scratches, and has no abrasive particles imbedded in it. Such a plate is easy to desensitize and resists scumming on the press. A poorly grained plate will have an uneven grain, full of bright spots and scratches. The platemaker considers such a plate "raw" since it is hard to desensitize and often develops scum on the press. Imbedded abrasive particles also cause trouble, since they lift out during platemaking and printing leaving pits that print as scum spots. Imbedding of abrasive in the grain can be prevented by using the proper abrasive and graining technique as described in LTF Bulletin No. 217, "The Standardization of Graining Procedures".

For a long time platemakers and pressmen had different ideas as to the fineness of the plate grain needed to produce the best printing plate. Platemakers preferred a fine grain because it would carry and print fine lines and halftones better than a coarse grain. On the other hand, pressmen preferred a coarse grain because it would carry more water and was easier to keep printing clean on the press. Aluminum and stainless steel plates were usually given a finer grain than zinc plates because of their greater ability to carry water. However, great improvements have been made in desensitization of plates as a result of research. Fine-grained zinc plates now print with a minimum of scumming trouble, and the quality of the printing produced is greatly improved. In fact, the desensitization of zinc and

Fine Grain on Zinc

Scratchy Zinc Grain

Medium Grain on Zinc

Irregular Zinc Grain

Coarse Zinc Grain

Typical Example of Imbedded
Quartz Abrasive in Poor Grain

Figure 16. These are fifty times enlarged photographs (phc.omicrographs) of good and bad plate grains. The bad grains are shown at the right.

aluminum plates is now so effective that deep-etch plates can be made on ungrained zinc and aluminum, and their printing quality is excellent.

Unfortunately, an ungrained plate can be used only once as such. To remove the deep-etched image the plate has to be grained. But after that it can be regrained and used again several times. The special steps necessary in making ungrained deep-etch plates are included in this text. They apply also to so-called brush-grained plates which are now supplied commercially. These have an extremely fine grain produced with a nylon brush and fine abrasive.

Freshly grained plates are always the best. Grained zinc and aluminum plates tend to oxidize, especially if they are stored in a damp place. The oxide film that is formed is hard to remove, especially if it is contaminated with grease which is always present in the shop atmosphere. Grained plates should always be stored face to face with a sheet of *dry* paper in between. Plate oxidation can be largely prevented, however, if the plate grainer will use a two per cent solution of sodium bichromate instead of plain water in producing the finish grain (see LTF Bulletin No. 217).

Graining has no effect on the flatness of zinc plates. But the graining of aluminum and stainless steel plates tends to spread the grained surface and make the plate buckle or bulge upward. This effect is less the finer the grain and the thicker the plate. This is another reason why aluminum and stainless steel plates are usually given a finer grain than zinc plates. This tendency to buckle can be reduced by graining both sides of the plate.

For complete information on the plate-graining process and the qualities of grain, see LTF Bulletin No. 217, "The Standardization of Graining Procedures".

When bimetal plates were first introduced, it was thought that they had to have a surface grain like that used on zinc and aluminum plates. But it was found that the copper-chromium and copper-stainless steel combinations worked equally well without a grain, and the smooth plates printed halftones of higher quality. Bimetal plates are now supplied without a grain except on special order. Copper-aluminum and copper-stainless steel bimetal plates are also generally supplied without grain.

For many years lithographers have argued about the comparative advantages of zinc and aluminum plates. In the past, zinc has been the more popular metal. But in recent years the use of aluminum plates has been increasing due, at least partly, to the excellent printing qualities of copperized aluminum deep-etched plates. Both metals have advantages and disadvantages, and the use of either one requires experience for the best results. The kind of work being printed often determines which metal is best.

Zinc and aluminum are similar in many ways. The deep-etch platemaking process is essentially the same for both with only a few differences. The two metals, however, have certain different properties that affect their printing qualities and handling on the press. Aluminum plates are somewhat more expensive than zinc in the smaller sizes, but cheaper in the larger sizes. The difference in cost is not an important factor.

Zinc is somewhat more grease-receptive than aluminum. This quality makes it easier to add work on zinc plates with tusche (an emulsified ink that can be applied to the plate with a pen or brush). Zinc and aluminum plates have about the same hardness, but zinc stretches more before it breaks. Because of this property, the pressman can stretch a zinc plate on the press more than he can an aluminum plate.

The stretchability of zinc plates makes it possible for the pressman to correct a misregister condition by stretching a plate on the press cylinder. This is not good practice and should be done only in emergencies. Any such stretch will remain permanently. All zinc plates take on some permanent stretch in the round-the-cylinder direction once they are on the press. Thus, if one of a set of four-color plates goes bad during printing and has to be remade, it is very difficult to make it register with the older plates. Often the entire set has to be remade. Aluminum plates don't take on any such permanent stretch.

Aluminum plates weigh less than half as much as zinc plates and are less cumbersome to handle. But aluminum plates must be handled carefully to avoid kinking, since kinks once formed will never flatten out completely.

Aluminum is the whiter and brighter of the two metals. This makes the image areas of the plate, especially fine details, more visible to the operator. Aluminum, being naturally more water-receptive than zinc, can be more easily and completely desensitized. Aluminum plates are easier to keep running clean and sharp on the press. For the same reason it is more difficult to add work on finished plates with tusche. Aluminum plates are somewhat sensitive to chlorides which tend to make them oxidize. In locations where the water supply is unusually high in chloride content, lithographers using them may have trouble with scum due to oxidation.

The natural differences in ink and water receptivity of zinc and aluminum plates, however, have largely been removed through the development of improved surface treatments and platemaking procedures. The only important differences that remain are in the greater brightness and lightness of aluminum, and in its resistance to stretching.

Stainless steel plates are used principally in metal decorating, and seldom in lithographing on paper. They are somewhat heavier than zinc plates, but approximately three times as hard and strong. Because of their hardness, the grain on stainless steel plates has good wearing qualities. Their great hardness and strength make them springy, and hard to make lie flat on the plate cylinder. They hold their size even better than aluminum plates. In metal decorating where the average press size is smaller than in commercial lithography on paper, the difficulties in handling stainless steel plates are compensated for by their long life and ability to hold image dimensions.

Chapter 5

COUNTER-ETCHING THE PLATE

All grained lithographic plates must be *counter-etched*. This is done by treating the grained surface with a weak acid solution that chemically attacks and cleans it. The purpose of counter-etching is three-fold:

1. To remove any residue of dirt or graining mud.
2. To remove any excess oxide from the metal surface.
3. To remove any trace of grease that contaminates the plate surface.

The term "counter-etch" is peculiar to lithography. In lithographic language an "etch" is a material or treatment that desensitizes the plate surface to ink. A desensitizing etch (plate etch) consists of a gum, an acid, and one or more salts. Counter-etching, then, is any treatment that "counteracts" the effect of an etch and sensitizes the plate or makes it receptive to ink. Actually, counter-etching affects the entire plate surface, cleaning it and making it receptive to either greasy ink, water, or gum, depending on which is applied first.

Smooth or ungrained plates for deep-etch don't have to be counter-etched. The preparatory treatment which consists of scrubbing them with powdered pumice and water cleans and sensitizes them sufficiently. Brush-grained plates supplied by trade shops should be counter-etched. But if the brush graining is done in the shop just before coating, no counter-etching is needed.

Counter-Etching Materials

The counter-etches most commonly used on zinc, aluminum and stainless steel plates are:

45

1. A solution containing one ounce of concentrated Hydro-chloric acid (37.0–38.5% HCl) in a gallon of water.

2. A solution containing six ounces of 99% acetic acid in a gallon of water.

Other acids have been and are being used. Those that make successful counter-etches seem to be acids that form salts with the plate metals that are soluble in water and are washed away. Acids such as phosphoric or chromic that form insoluble metallic salts, or that are adsorbed (tightly held) on the metal surface, don't work well as counter-etches. Examples of other counter-etching acids are citric acid, hydrofluoric acid, and mixtures of nitric acid and alum (potassium aluminum sul-fate). Citric acid and nitric acid-alum counter-etches are used on zinc plates. Citric acid and hydrofluoric acid counter-etches are used on aluminum plates.

LTF recommends both the hydrochloric and acetic acid counter-etches for zinc plates. For aluminum plates, the acetic acid counter-etch is the better of the two. The hydrochloric acid counter-etch is probably better for stainless steel plates.

Method of Counter-Etching

In LTF's studies the following method has been found best for counter-etching grained plates:

1. Flush the plate with water and clean the grain as thor-oughly as possible by rubbing with a cotton, molleton, or flannel pad under running water.

Figure 17. Counter-etching the plate.

2. Drain the water off the plate, and flood it with the counter-etch solution. Rock the plate back and forth for about a minute to get complete and uniform coverage and to keep the counter-etch in motion.

3. Drain off the counter-etch and flush the plate with water to wash off the remainder. Then scrub the plate again with cotton, molleton or flannel under running water to remove anything formed or loosened by the action of the counter-etch. Finally go over the plate lightly with a scrub brush to remove any lint adhering to the grain.

While you may use different counter-etching solutions for zinc, aluminum, or stainless steel plates, the actual steps and technique of counter-etching are the same for all three metals.

Discussion

In counter-etching zinc plates, the weak hydrochloric and acetic acid solutions attack the surface of the metal chemically and dissolve the oxide and a little of the metallic zinc. If continued long enough, this action would destroy the grain. The object, therefore, is to let the acid work just long enough to remove the oxide and to loosen any dirt and grease so that it can be flushed off with water. The grain structure should remain essentially unchanged.

Scrubbing the plate with a brush or pad while the counter-etch is still on it should be avoided. The reason is that scrubbing concentrates the action of the acid on the peaks of the grain and rounds them off, while the valleys where most of the dirt lies receive little action. Brush bristles are too large

Figure 18. One brush bristle on a grained plate, both magnified 50 times.

to reach down into the grain valleys and clean them out. But, if the counter-etch is allowed to act on the plate without scrubbing, the difference in chemical attack on the peaks and valleys is much less. The counter-etch can then clean out the valleys without, at the same time, seriously damaging the peaks.

*   *   *   *   *

In counter-etching aluminum plates there is much less chemical action than on zinc plates. Aluminum is very reactive to the oxygen of the air. As soon as it is exposed to air, it becomes covered with a thin protective film of aluminum oxide. This film adheres tightly and is quite impervious and chemically inactive. It resists further oxidation and keeps the aluminum from being attacked by all but a very few acids.

The object in counter-etching aluminum plates is not to remove the aluminum oxide film. It is only to attack the oxide film superficially, and just enough to loosen any attached dirt and grease. Acetic acid does this best. Hydrochloric and particularly hydrofluoric acid attack the oxide film too rapidly. They are likely to penetrate it. And if they do, they violently

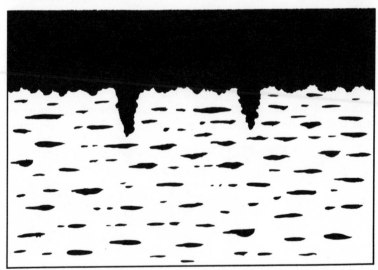

Figure 19. This drawing shows the cross section of an aluminum plate with pits produced by a counter-etch that breaks through the surface film of aluminum oxide.

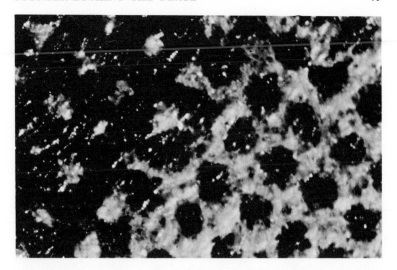

Figure 20. Photomicrograph showing ink-dot (oxidation) scum on an aluminum plate.

attack the metallic aluminum and produce pits in the grain. These pits are almost impossible to desensitize. They show up, either on the finished plate or during printing as fine ink spots, a form of scum typical of aluminum plates and generally called "oxidation scum" or "ink-dot scum". Even with acetic acid counter-etch, it is best to avoid scrubbing with a bristle brush while the acid is on the plate.

*   *   *   *   *

Abrasive particles imbedded in the plate grain are a cause of scum. Imbedding of abrasive during graining is likely to be worse on aluminum than on zinc plates. The imbedded particles can usually be seen through a magnifier or microscope. If they are not removed during the counter-etching, they become dislodged during printing, leaving undesensitized pits that accumulate ink and eventually print as scum spots. Proper counter-etching and thorough cleaning of the plate after it is counter-etched are necessary to remove imbedded abrasive. The real problem goes back to the graining operation where the condition should be corrected (see LTF Bulletin No. 217).

The counter-etching of stainless steel plates is the same as for zinc plates.

Chapter 6

PLATE SURFACE PRE-TREATMENTS

The grained and counter-etched plate can be coated directly with the light-sensitive bichromated gum coating without any chemical pre-treatment and this is done in many shops. LTF's researches however, have shown that for grained zinc plates, a treatment with *Cronak* solution before coating prevents certain difficulties in platemaking and makes a considerably better plate. Another treatment, *Pre-etching,* is helpful at times. For grained aluminum plates, no treatment is usually necessary between counter-etching and coating, but under certain circumstances a treatment with *Brunak* solution is helpful.

These treatments prior to coating the plate are called *pre-treatments* to distinguish them from similar treatments of the non-image areas after the bichromated gum stencil has been removed. The latter are referred to as *post-treatments.* Chemical pre-treatments are for both *grained* and *ungrained* zinc plates, and for grained aluminum plates. They are not recommended for *stainless steel* plates or for *grainless* aluminum plates. In this chapter we will discuss the above three chemical pre-treatments, and also the mechanical pre-treatment of grainless zinc and aluminum plates.

PRE-CRONAK

The purpose of the Pre-Cronak treatment for zinc plates is to produce a very thin brownish coating on the grained surface. This coating does several things:

50

1. It prevents oxidation or corrosion of the zinc surface by oxygen from the air. Oxidized plates can't be well desensitized and tend to scum both in platemaking and in printing. Plate oxidation occurs more rapidly the higher the temperature and humidity. It was very troublesome in the army's topographic work in the South Pacific during World War II but was overcome completely by use of the Cronak treatment.

2. It makes the plate easier to coat, develop and clear.

3. It improves desensitization of the non-image areas.

4. On Cronaked zinc plates the deep-etch image is sharper. Both printing quality and life are improved.

The chemistry of the Cronak treatment is not thoroughly understood. But the Cronak film seems to consist of a gelatinous combination of two chromium oxides, Cr_2O_3 and CrO_3, and some water. It is only about two millionths of an inch thick, but it sticks very tightly to the zinc. You will find more about its chemistry in LTF Bulletin No. 401, "Chemistry of Lithography".

The Cronak Solution

	Metric Units	U. S. Units
Ammonium Bichromate		
[$(NH_4)_2Cr_2O_7$], Photo Grade	360 g.	12 avoir. oz. (340 g.)
Water	20 liters	5 gallons
Sulfuric Acid (H_2SO_4), Sp. Gr. 1.84	64 cc.	2 liq. oz. (59 cc.)

The pH value (acidity) of the finished solution should be between 1.4 and 1.7. In making this solution it is very important that you dissolve the ammonium bichromate in the water first. Then add the sulfuric acid slowly while stirring the solution. Never add the water to the strong sulfuric acid as this might cause an explosion and injure you. For other precautions in making and handling the Cronak Solution, see Chapter 3, page 23.

Method of Cronaking Plates

To Cronak a plate you simply let the Cronak solution act on the counter-etched plate for a short time. There are two ways to do this:

TREATMENT IN THE SINK. With the properly prepared plate in the sink, drain off the excess water. Then lower the grid so

Figure 21. Flood the plate as quickly as possible with the Cronak solution.

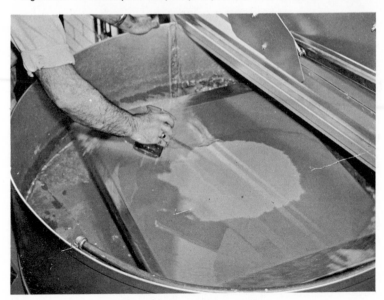

Figure 22. In the whirler start pouring the Cronak solution at one edge and continue pouring across the plate.

that the plate will be level. Put the Cronak solution in two wide-mouth bottles and proceed as follows:

1. Holding the two bottles, one in each hand, dump the Cronak solution onto the plate, first from one side and then from the other. The idea is to cover the plate with solution as quickly as possible. Let the solution stand on the plate for thirty seconds to one minute.

2. Flush the Cronak solution off the plate until the wash water shows no yellow color.

3. With water running on the plate, go over the surface with a wad of wet cotton, rubbing lightly. Flush the plate again with water and drain off the excess.

When this is done, the plate is ready to be coated.

TREATMENT IN THE WHIRLER. Place the properly prepared plate in a horizontal whirler. Rotate the whirler at 25 to 30 rpm (revolutions per minute). Flood the plate with water and allow the excess to whirl off for about fifteen seconds. Then proceed as follows:

1. Pour the Cronak solution rapidly onto the plate, starting at one edge and continuing across to the opposite edge. Stop the whirler as soon as the plate is covered and allow the solution to stand on the plate for thirty seconds to one minute.

2. Flush the Cronak solution off the plate until no more yellow color comes off in the wash water.

3. With water running on the plate, go over it with a wad of cotton, rubbing lightly. Flush the plate again with water and whirl off the excess.

The plate is now ready to be coated.

Discussion

The object in flooding the plate quickly with Cronak solution is to produce uniform action and a uniform film over the entire plate. Cronaking changes the color of zinc plates to a light tan or brown. If the action isn't uniform, some parts of the plate will be darker than others. The chances are this wouldn't make any difference in the plate's printing quality, but it looks bad.

The depth of color of a Cronaked plate depends on how long the Cronak solution acts on its surface. The longer you let the plate stand with the solution on it, the darker the color will be. The Cronak treatment, however, is so effective in preventing plate oxidation that a very light tan color is all that is necessary in most cases. Drying the Cronaked plate before coating it is not necessary.

If you are making small plates, it is practical to Cronak them in a tray. Just place some Cronak solution in the tray and immerse the plate in it for thirty seconds, then take the plate out and wash it under running water. This system makes it possible to treat a number of plates in the same Cronak bath. But it will take longer for them to reach the same color as the solution gets weaker. When the pH of the bath goes up above 2.0, most of its activity has been lost. You can rejuvenate it once by adding enough more sulfuric acid to lower the pH to 1.4 to 1.7 again, but the second time it goes up to 2.0 it should be discarded.

You can tell pretty well when the Cronak solution has become too weak by the time it takes to give the plates the light tan color. If it takes longer than about one minute, the solution should be rejuvenated or discarded.

The Cronak treatment is not very effective on plates that have already become oxidized. And if plates stand for some time after graining before they are used, they are likely to oxidize. This is especially true in hot, humid weather. There are two good ways to prevent grained zinc plates from oxidizing before the platemaker gets them:

1. The use of sodium bichromate as a two per cent solution instead of plain water in the graining machine (see Chapter 4, page 42).

2. Cronaking the plates immediately after they are grained and before storing or shipping them.

In either case, however, the plates should be counter-etched and Cronaked by the platemaker just like ordinary grained plates.

PRE-BRUNAK

The purpose of the Pre-Brunak treatment for aluminum plates is to reinforce their normal oxide film and make them even more resistant to oxidation. But, since aluminum plates are more resistant to troublesome oxidation than zinc plates, the Brunak treatment can usually be omitted. LTF recommends it for use only when there is trouble with oxidation scum. This trouble usually occurs during periods of hot, humid weather.

The chemistry of the Brunak treatment is not understood. However, tests have shown that it increases the resistance of aluminum plates to oxidation and is helpful in hot, humid summer weather. This seems to be its only advantage. Pre-Brunaking doesn't make the plate easier to coat, develop or clear. It doesn't seem to increase the desensitization or to improve the quality or life of aluminum plates. For more about the chemistry of the Brunak treatment, see LTF Bulletin No. 401, "Chemistry of Lithography".

The Brunak Solution

	Metric Units	U. S. Units
Ammonium Bichromate		
$[(NH_4)_2Cr_2O_7]$, Photo Grade	1350 g.	45 avoir. oz.
Water	20 liters	5 gallons
Hydrofluoric Acid (HF), 48%	160 cc.	5 liq. oz. (150 cc.)

Remember that the fumes of strong hydrofluoric acid are poisonous. Remember also that hydrofluoric acid attacks glass, porcelain, and stoneware. For precautions in handling it, see Chapter 3, page 25.

The amount of hydrofluoric acid in the finished Brunak solution is so small that it attacks glass rather slowly. So the solution can be mixed in glass bottles if it is to be used immediately. But to store it, you should use one-gallon or larger polyethylene bottles.

The fact that the Brunak solution attacks glass rules out the use of glass-electrode pH meters for finding its pH value.

Method of Brunaking Plates

To Brunak an aluminum plate you simply allow the Brunak solution to act on the counter-etched plate for a short time. The method is exactly the same as in Cronaking zinc plates except that the time of the action is longer. Follow the instructions on page 51. But instead of thirty seconds to one minute, let the Brunak solution act on the plate for one to two minutes depending on the depth of color you desire.

DISCUSSION. As in the Cronak treatment, quick flooding of

the plate with the Brunak solution is necessary to produce uniform action and a uniform color. Brunaking changes the color of aluminum plates to tan or brown, depending on how long the action takes place. A properly Brunaked plate will have a uniform, very light tan color.

As soon as a plate has been Brunaked and washed, it is ready to be coated with the light-sensitive deep-etch coating. Drying the Brunaked plate before coating it is not necessary.

If you are making small plates you can Brunak them by immersing them in a tray of the solution, and use the same solution for a number of plates. (The tray should be of hard rubber or plastic. Glass or porcelain trays will be attacked and will weaken the solution.) But, since you can't tell when the solution is exhausted by measuring its pH value, you simply have to discard it when it no longer will give the plates the desired light tan color after about two minutes immersion.

As we said before, aluminum plates are normally covered with an invisible film of aluminum oxide. This does no harm. But, if a plate was dried too slowly or was subjected to dampness during storage it will show a powdery oxide on the surface. Such a plate will not be helped by Brunaking and should be regrained before use.

Pre-Cronaking is an important step in making ungrained zinc plates, but Pre-Brunaking has not been found helpful as a treatment for ungrained aluminum plates. Both zinc and aluminum require a special mechanical pre-treatment to prepare them for coating. This treatment is also described in this chapter.

PRE-ETCHING

Pre-etching is the treatment of a grained and counter-etched plate with a desensitizing etch (see Introduction to this chapter) just before applying the light-sensitive bichromated gum coating. Its purpose is to produce a very thin gum film on the metal surface. The light-sensitive coating adheres to this film.

Ordinarily pre-etching is of no help in making deep-etch plates. But in hot, humid weather, the deep-etch stencil is sometimes very hard to scrub off. Under these conditions, pre-etching is a help since the hardened stencil doesn't adhere as tightly to a pre-etched plate. Pre-etching is therefore recommended only when the platemaker has difficulty in clearing his plates.

Pre-etching can be done on Cronaked zinc plates or Brunaked aluminum plates as well as on plain counter-etched plates.

The Pre-Etching Solution

The pre-etching solution is actually a desensitizing plate etch (see Chapter 3, page 35 and Appendix, page 216). Whatever plate etch is being used will serve the purpose.

Method of Pre-Etching Plates

Pre-etching can be done either in the sink or in a horizontal whirler, but it is usually done in the latter. Simply drain or whirl off the excess water and pour on a generous supply of the plate etch. Work the etch uniformly over the plate with a sponge or soft brush for one to two minutes. Then flush the plate and go over it with a wad of cotton under running water to remove all the etch that you can. When this is done, the plate is ready to be coated.

Discussion

In pre-etching it isn't necessary to dry the etch down before washing it off. Drying the etch would produce a stronger, tougher gum film but this isn't important in pre-etching.

Pre-etching is never necessary in making ungrained zinc or aluminum deep-etch plates or in making deep-etch plates on stainless steel.

PRE-TREATMENT OF UNGRAINED
ZINC AND ALUMINUM PLATES

One of the secrets in making grainless zinc and aluminum deep-etch plates lies in the preparation of the smooth metal surface. This preparation consists of scrubbing the metal surface with pumice powder and water. Its purpose is to thoroughly clean, degrease and slightly roughen the plate surface. It is a purely mechanical treatment. Unless it is done properly, the coating solution will not cover the surface uniformly and the dried coating will not adhere tightly enough.

This mechanical treatment or preparation of ungrained plates to receive the deep-etch coating is exactly the same for both zinc and aluminum. Zinc plates, of course, have to be Cronaked after this treatment.

Materials Required

The only materials you will need are F pumice powder and water, and Cronak solution for zinc plates.

Method of Preparing the Plate Surface

The best place in which to pre-treat grainless plates is the sink in which you do your counter-etching.

With the plate lying flat and level in the sink, sprinkle a liberal amount of pumice powder over its surface. Then, with a clean damp rag, scrub the surface thoroughly and uniformly. A good method is to rub the plate first from side to side, and then from front to back. Continue this scrubbing until the plate shows no sign of greasiness, in other words, until the surface wets uniformly. You can easily see any greasy areas because the water film will break and pull away from them.

When you have done this, flush off the pumice powder with

Figure 23. The surface of an ungrained plate must be cleaned and roughened by scrubbing it with pumice powder and water.

water, and wipe off the excess water with a clean rag or sponge. Now inspect the thin film of water left on the plate. It should remain continuous and not break or pull away from any area. If it does, the plate still has some greasiness. In this case, simply sprinkle on more pumice powder and repeat the scrubbing in the same way until the plate will hold a thin water film without any breaks occurring.

At this point the plate surface will have lost its polish and will have a satiny appearance. The next step is to make its texture uniform. You do this by re-dampening the plate, sprinkling on more pumice powder, and going over the surface lightly with a clean deep-etch developing pad that you use only for this purpose. Don't use too much water as this would lessen the abrasive action of the pumice. Give all areas at least three passes of the pad in each direction. Apply very little pressure to the pad. In fact, the weight of the pad itself gives enough pressure. This treatment will give the plate the desired uniform texture.

Finally, flush the plate thoroughly with tap water while going over it with a wad of cotton to get rid of all traces of pumice.

If the plate is zinc, it must be Cronaked before being coated (see Page 50). If it is aluminum, it is now ready to be coated, and no chemical pre-treatment is necessary or desirable.

Discussion

Proper preparation of the ungrained plate surface is very important. If grease or finger marks aren't completely removed, the light-sensitive coating won't be uniform and won't adhere properly. The slight tooth produced by the pumice powder anchors the coating and makes it stick tighter. Unless this surface preparation is done properly, the coating will have a tendency to chip or rub off during some of the later steps in platemaking.

The sink in which this plate preparation is done should have a drain that runs to a sump or catch basin. Otherwise the pumice powder, being heavy, will settle out and may eventually stop up the sewer. A catch basin will prevent the pumice from going into the sewer and can be cleaned out whenever it accumulates sediment.

Chapter 7

COATING AND DRYING THE PLATE

First, let's review briefly what has been said about the preparation of plates to receive the light-sensitive deep-etch coating. If the platemaker has followed LTF instructions, the different types of plates will have been treated as follows:

Grained zinc plates will have been counter-etched and Cronaked. The only exception would be that in hot, humid weather, they may also have been pre-etched.

Grained aluminum plates will have been counter-etched. The only exception is that in hot, humid weather, they may also have been Brunaked to prevent oxidation.

Stainless steel plates will have been counter-etched only.

Ungrained and brush-grained zinc and aluminum plates will have been cleaned and slightly roughened with abrasive and water. Zinc plates will have been Pre-Cronaked. Aluminum plates brush-grained by a trade shop will have been counter-etched. But if surface roughening was done as a preparation for coating, they will not have been counter-etched.

In each case, the surface preparation will have been done just before you are ready to coat the plate so that the plate surface will still be wet with water. Don't let it dry before you apply the coating. Allowing it to dry runs the risk of the surface again becoming contaminated with dust or grease from the atmosphere. This should be avoided.

The purpose of applying the deep-etch coating is to cover the plate surface with a light-sensitive bichromated gum film.

Then when the coated plate is exposed to an arc light through a positive, this film becomes hardened on the non-image areas and protects them while the image areas are being deep-etched, lacquered, and inked (see Introduction page 5). Coating the plate is a very important step in deep-etch platemaking. All succeeding steps depend on its being done properly.

THE DEEP-ETCH COATING SOLUTION

There are a number of good deep-etch coating solutions that can be bought from lithographic supply houses. Unless your shop makes a great many plates and employs a chemist or a man trained in preparing platemaking chemicals, it is better to buy the prepared coating solution than to try to make it.

All the known deep-etch coating solutions are similar in composition. There are slight differences in the proportions of ingredients, in Baumé density or specific gravity, in viscosity, and in pH value (see Chapter 2). At least one coating solution is made with a chemically treated gum arabic instead of the natural gum. Some coating solutions contain a dye (usually a blue dye that gives them a green color) while others do not. For the sake of discussion here, the following LTF formula can be considered typical.

Deep-Etch Coating Solution

	Metric Units	U. S. Units
Gum Arabic Solution, 14° Bé	720 cc.	3 quarts
Ammonium Bichromate		
$[(NH_4)_2Cr_2O_7]$, Stock Solution	240 cc.	1 quart
Ammonium Hydroxide, 28% NH_3	36 cc.	4¾ liq. oz. (140 cc.)

Detailed instructions for making the gum arabic solution and the ammonium bichromate stock solution, and for preparing and testing the coating solution, will be found in the Appendix.

METHOD OF COATING GRAINED PLATES

To coat the prepared grained plate, first place it in the whirler and set the whirler speed at 45 to 65 rpm, depending on the plate size. (Small plates, up to 22 x 34 inches, can be coated at 65 rpm. Very large plates can be coated better at 45 rpm.) Flush the plate again with a large volume of water at a controlled temperature (preferably 85 or 90° F.) and whirl off the excess.

After shutting off the water, let the plate whirl for a definite time (for example, 30 seconds), then pour on the coating solution.

The coating solution should always be kept at room temperature, never in a refrigerator. When cold, the solution is too thick to spread evenly and give coatings of uniform thickness.

The amount of coating solution required will depend on the size of the plate and the type of whirler used. The following table shows the approximate amounts you will need for *grained plates* of different sizes:

| | Volume of Coating Solution | |
Plate Size	Horizontal Whirler	Vertical Whirler
14 x 20 inches	3 ounces	2 ounces
17 x 22 "	4 "	3 "
23 x 29 "	7 "	5 "
23 x 36 "	8 "	6 "
30 x 42 "	11 "	8 "
36 x 48 "	15 "	11 "
42 x 58 "	20 "	14 "
42 x 65 "	22 "	15 "
51 x 73 "	30 "	21 "
52½ x 77 "	32 "	22 "

These are generous amounts. With experience you may find that you can cut them down somewhat.

There are a number of different ways to apply coating solution to the plate. The following methods are good and are recommended:

Figure 24. Coating the plate on a horizontal whirler.

1. For small to medium-sized plates, start pouring at the center of the plate. You can either pour all the solution on the center of the plate, or start pouring at the center and move toward the edge as the pool spreads.

2. For medium to very large plates, start pouring at the edge and move to the center of the plate. This insures covering the corners.

Figure 25. Coating the plate on a vertical whirler.

In either case, hold the container as close to the plate as possible and pour the coating in a steady stream. If you move the container as you pour, do so at such a rate that the solution will be used up by the time you reach the end of your motion, namely, at the edge of the plate if you started at the center, or at the center if you started at the edge.

When all the coating is on, speed up the whirler, if possible, to about 65 rpm. This is a good speed for drying the plate. Of course, if your whirler doesn't have a variable speed drive, continue to whirl at the same speed.

Next, close the whirler, turn on the heat, and allow the plate to whirl until dry. As soon as it is dry, remove it from the whirler.

The coating is now light sensitive and should be protected from direct rays of white light. This can be done by keeping it covered with a sheet of yellow or orange paper (goldenrod paper) until you are ready to give it the image-forming exposure.

METHOD OF COATING UNGRAINED PLATES

Ungrained and brush-grained zinc and aluminum plates require a much thinner coating than grained plates. You obtain this thinner coating mainly by thinning or diluting your regular deep-etch coating solution. Simply use a 2:1 mixture of coating solution and water—in other words, dilute the regular coating solution with half its volume of water. Thus, if the regular coating solution had a Baumé of 14.0, the diluted coating solution for ungrained plates will have a Baumé of 12.0. For a brush-grained plate you will need only one-half to two-thirds the amount of this diluted coating solution as that shown in the Table (Page 62) for a tub-grained plate of the same size.

The whirler speed for both coating and drying brush-grained plates should be about 75 rpm. Otherwise, all operations are the same as for tub-grained plates. The only difference you will find is that the thinner coating dries much faster. Also, after exposure, the plates develop faster.

Discussion

The ammonium hydroxide is put in the deep-etch coating solution to stabilize it. Without ammonia the solution would become useless very quickly. But as the coating dries on the plate, the ammonia gradually evaporates. As it evaporates, the coating becomes more light sensitive and less stable. If the plate isn't exposed and developed within a reasonable time, the coating will become too insoluble to be developed and the plate will be useless. Heat speeds up this deterioration. This is why the plate should be taken from the whirler just as soon as it is dry.

*   *   *   *

The plate whirler is a machine with a rotating table on which the plate should lie perfectly flat. In some whirlers the table is horizontal; in others it is almost vertical. Both types are suitable. Most whirlers nowadays have a variable-speed drive which can be adjusted to change the thickness of the coating. To obtain a thicker coating, you lower the speed; for a thinner coating, you increase the speed.

Every whirler should have a source of water for flushing the plate just before you coat it. And it is very important that the water be temperature controlled. The best idea is to have both hot and cold water piped to the whirler and install a constant-

Figure 26. A constant temperature mixing valve will deliver water at any temperature for which it is set.

temperature mixing valve. Once properly set, this valve will supply water at the same temperature all the time. This temperature should be one that you can maintain the year round. Usually 85 or 90° F. is satisfactory.

If you don't have a constant temperature mixing valve, you should still supply both hot and cold water to the whirler, and adjust the valves manually to supply water at the right temperature.

Controlling the temperature of the water used to flush the plate just before you coat it controls the temperature of the plate. This is most important. A cold plate cools the coating solution, makes it flow more slowly, and slows down the drying. The reverse is true if the plate is warm. The only way you can keep the coating thickness uniform from plate to plate is to control the plate's temperature.

Most modern whirlers have heating elements to heat the air and speed up the drying of the coating. Some whirlers have forced ventilation for the same purpose.

*   *   *   *

For successful results in producing plates day after day, it is most important that the coatings be free from blemishes and uniform in thickness. The most common types of blemishes are described in the following paragraphs.

Sunburst effects or streaks running from the center to the edges of the plate. These are caused by (1) greasiness of the plate surface (improper preparation for coating) or (2) solid or jelly-like particles suspended in the coating solution. If the cause is greasiness of the plate, the coating should be washed off with water and the plate re-prepared for coating by counter-etching, Cronaking, Brunaking or treatment with pumice powder as the case may be (see Chapters 5 and 6). It can then be re-coated. If the radial streaks still show up in the dried coating, the trouble is probably due to solid or gelatinous particles. In this case try a new batch of coating solution.

Pinholes in the coating caused by air bubbles in the coating solution, are formed by pouring the solution onto the plate too rapidly or from too great a height. To avoid air bubbles in the coating solution, never shake the container or stir the solution rapidly. When you transfer it to the vessel you use to pour it onto the plate, do so carefully, pouring it down the side of the vessel to avoid splashing.

Some platemakers find it helpful to strain the coating solution when they transfer it from the original container to the pouring vessel. They use several layers of damp cheesecloth in a funnel for this purpose. To prevent bubbles from forming when the solution drops from the funnel into the container, they put a piece of wet string through the funnel tube so that it hangs down and touches the bottom or side of the receiving vessel. In this way the strained solution runs down the string and no bubbles are formed.

Usually it is a good idea to let the coating solution stand for a while in the vessel before pouring it onto the plate. Any bub-

Figure 27. To remove possible sediment strain the coating solution through several thicknesses of slightly damp cheesecloth.

bles formed will then rise to the top and you can skim them off with a piece of blotter or absorbent paper. Some platemakers get around the bubble problem by putting the coating solution in a vessel with a bottom outlet. The vessel is hung or set on a shelf, and a rubber tube attached to the bottom outlet is used to deliver the solution to the plate.

After the plate has been coated and whirled for about one minute, you can stop the whirler and examine the wet coating for bubbles. If only a few appear, you can break them with a toothpick or sharpened stick and continue the whirling. But if there are many bubbles, it is best to wash the coating off and start over, taking care to prevent bubbles from forming.
Comet-shaped spots in the coating can be caused by a number of things. Sometimes bubbles will cause them. But the most common causes are:

1. A few solid or gelatinous particles in the coating solution. These could be fibers, undissolved dye, or dirt from the gum arabic. They can usually be gotten rid of by carefully straining the solution through damp cheesecloth.

Figure 28a. A good method of applying the deep-etch coating. Feeding solution from the bottom of the can through a tube prevents bubbles in the coating.

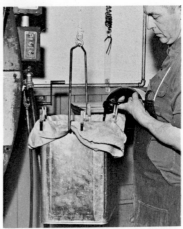

Figure 28b. A gallon or more of coating solution is strained into the can reservoir where it is always ready to be used.

2. Lint adhering to the plate grain. This can be prevented by going over the plate lightly with a bristle brush under running water before you apply the coating.

3. Dust from the air, particles from the ceiling, or particles from a dirty whirler dropping on the plate. If the air is dusty, keep the whirler lid closed. Use a filter at the air intake if the whirler has forced circulation. Paint or cover the ceiling above the whirler to prevent dropping of dirt particles. Clean the whirler every day, especially the lid.

4. Sediment in the water used in flooding and rinsing the plate. If the water contains sediment, install a filter in the water system.

*   *   *   *

After the plate has been coated, most platemakers use heat to speed up the drying. Heat is not always necessary. If the relative humidity is below 50 per cent, the coating will dry fairly quickly and thoroughly without it. But, if the relative humidity is above 50 per cent, the drying may be too slow and may not be thorough. The higher the relative humidity, the slower and less thorough the drying will be. So heat should always be used when the relative humidity is above 50 per cent.

Whenever you use heat in the whirler, there are two important precautions to be taken. The first is, never let the temperature in the whirler get above 110° F. If it does, there is danger of the coating becoming so hard that it can't be developed after the light exposure. The second precaution is, never leave the plate in the warm whirler after the coating is dry. This, too, would harden the coating and make it difficult or impossible to develop. A good idea is to insert a thermometer through the lid of your whirler as far from the heating elements as possible, and shut off the heat as soon as it indicates 110° F. Then examine the plate at intervals of a few minutes and remove it as soon as the coating is dry. When you have done this and have found the time it takes for the plate to dry, you can time the whole operation from closing the whirler to taking out the plate by the clock.

Probably the best system is to use heat in the whirler at all times, regardless of the relative humidity. This saves time. It has the advantage also that the platemaker develops a routine that becomes a habit and is the same for all plates. He doesn't have to change from one system to another whenever the relative humidity goes above or below 50 per cent.

If the plateroom is air conditioned, this is a great help to the platemaker. In such a room the relative humidity is held constant within a very few per cent and there are no special precautions to be taken in summertime. Many troubles that result from changing relative humidity and temperature cease to exist and the platemaker's work is simplified, speeded up, and improved in quality.

Many shops don't have air-conditioned plate rooms. And because the temperature and relative humidity change from day to day and from season to season, the platemaker must make certain adjustments and take special precautions in order to produce satisfactory plates. His job is more complicated, production at times is hampered, and the quality of plates is not as uniform as it should be.

Most of the trouble arises when the relative humidity goes above 65 or 70 per cent as it often does in the summertime. When this happens, plates won't dry thoroughly in the whirler without heat. The coating remains sticky. Even when dried with heat, the coating picks up moisture from the atmosphere and becomes sticky when the plate is taken out of the whirler and allowed to cool to room temperature. This won't do because the positives and also the gaskets of the photocomposing machine stick to the coating and damage it when they are pulled loose. Later on these areas are penetrated by the deep-etching solution so that the plate scums.

How then, can the platemaker prevent stickiness of the coating on days when the relative humidity is high? There are several alternatives, all of which aim at protecting the dried coating from atmospheric moisture. None of them are foolproof, and the results they give will depend on the care and experience of the platemaker. These methods are as follows:

1. When you take the plate out of the whirler, and while it is still warm, quickly apply a paste wax to the coating, rubbing it down thin and smooth with a soft rag. Any good paste floor wax will do. (Don't use a "self-polishing" wax as this is a water emulsion and will remove the coating.) Many platemakers call this "Simonizing" the plate. The wax film remains on the coating during the light exposure. After that you can leave it on or wash it off with gasoline or naphtha. Leaving it on doesn't hinder development very much.

2. While the plate is still warm, apply a deep-etch lacquer, rubbing it down to a thin smooth film. In this case, however, it is usually necessary to remove the lacquer film after the exposure and just before development. It is hard to get the developer to penetrate the lacquer film.

3. While the plate is still warm, apply a thin, even film of asphaltum to the coating, and fan it thoroughly dry. This asphaltum film doesn't have to be removed before development. In fact, there is an advantage in leaving it on. It remains on the light-hardened stencil and gives it additional resistance to penetration by the developer, deep-etching solution, and washing alcohol.

Just remember that these wax, lacquer, and asphaltum films are very thin and are not completely impervious to atmospheric moisture. They simply retard the absorption of moisture by the light-sensitive deep-etch coating before and during the exposure. They will usually protect the coating for a reasonable time while plates remain on the photocomposing machine. But eventually the coating will pick up enough moisture to become tacky.

If your plates are to receive only a single exposure in a vacuum printing frame, no moisture-resistant film of wax, lacquer or asphaltum is usually necessary. Simply remove the plate from the whirler and lay it in the printing frame while it is still warm. Lay the flat on the plate in the required position, close the printing frame and proceed with the exposure. You may have to increase the exposure somewhat, but if the positives are dense and sharp, you may not have any trouble.

Chapter 8

LIGHT SENSITIVITY OF DEEP-ETCH COATINGS

The fact that Alois Senefelder invented lithography between 1796 and 1800 is well known because he obtained a patent and wrote a book describing his process in great detail. But a great many changes and improvements have been made since Senefelder's time. If he could visit a present day lithographic shop, he would hardly recognize his process. Unfortunately the names of those who contributed these improvements have been forgotten.

Probably the most important development has been that of photolithography—the use of photographic negatives and positives to produce printing images on lithographic printing plates. It took the efforts of many workers over 100 years to make photolithography practical and bring it to its present state of workability.

About 1832, a French chemist named Vauquellin discovered that, under certain conditions, potassium bichromate ($K_2Cr_2O_7$) was reduced by sunlight to form chromic oxide (Cr_2O_3). Mungo Ponton, in 1839, sensitized paper with potassium bichromate, exposed it to sunlight, and produced the first photograph. Between 1841 and 1860 several workers experimented with mixtures of bichromate with gelatin, glue and albumin as light-sensitive coatings on paper and lithographic stones. Their work laid the basis for gravure printing, photo engraving, and photolithography. Exactly what each invented, and when, is hard to determine since they kept their discoveries secret and sometimes didn't disclose them until several years later. Poitevin and Fox Talbot are generally credited with producing photolithographic images on stone using bichromated gelatin and glue in 1855. Lemercier, who worked with Poitevin, is thought to have originated the well-known bichromated albumin process. James and Osborne produced photolithographic transfers about 1859. They coated paper with bichromated gelatin or glue, made contact prints from negatives, inked the exposed coating, and developed the prints in water. These prints were used in the same way as hand transfers (see Introduction, page 3).

The first true deep-etch plates are credited to Frederic Sears although the British patent was applied for in 1904 in the names of Joseph and Donald Swan who financed his experiments. Apparently the Sears process presented difficulties and was not considered practical.

In 1918, G. Douglas, Superintendent of the Photo-Process Office of the Survey of Egypt, developed a process using bichromated gum arabic for making plates directly from charts, maps, etc. The process was called "Douglagraph". While the plates were not intentionally deep-etched, this process was the true forerunner of the gum deep-etch process of today.

The first deep-etch processes to come into general use in this country were those developed by Julius Bekk and F. H. Hausleiter in Germany. Bekk's process, known as "Beka Offset-Deep" was introduced about 1930. It used bichromated glue as the plate coating. Hausleiter's process, which used bichromated gum arabic, came about 1931.

The Bartel, Hanco, Harris, Lith-Kem-Ko, Litho. Research, LTF, McKinley, Neusel, Pitman, Schultz, Sinvalco, and other deep-etch processes are similar to Hausleiter's process.

* * * *

Two things are common to all photolithographic processes —a bichromate and a colloid. By colloid we mean a material of large molecular size that can form a uniform, continuous film. The particular colloids of value in photolithography are water soluble. When mixed with a bichromate, coated on a stone or plate, and exposed to light through a negative or positive, the parts receiving the light become insoluble. When the unexposed parts are washed away in development, a photographic image remains. Albumin and casein are the colloids mostly used in making "surface" plates (plates made with negatives). Gum arabic is the colloid used in this country for making deep-etch plates. In some foreign countries bichromated glue is still used for this purpose.

It is interesting to note that all the early developments in photolithography were made with little or no knowledge of the chemical reactions involved. The inventors relied entirely on cut-and-try experiments. However, lithographers ran into many problems in using photolithography, particularly the uncertainty of results. It was obvious, therefore, that photolithographic platemaking needed carefully planned chemical research before it could attain its maximum dependability and usefulness.

Since about 1900 many chemists have studied the reactions by which bichromated colloids become insoluble under the influence of light. But these reactions are so complex that, even now, we can't write chemical equations for them. In the first place the colloids—albumin, casein, gum arabic, etc.—are such complex materials that we can't give them chemical formulas. In fact, they are not pure chemicals but mixtures. In the second place, when bichromate is added to one of these colloids and the mixture exposed to light as it is in platemaking, only a small fraction of the bichromate becomes changed. Chemical analysis shows that the changed part has been reduced and part of its oxygen taken away. We assume that this oxygen is taken up by the colloid which becomes oxidized. In some way the reduction product of the bichromate [Cr_2O_3 or $Cr_2(OH)_6$] attaches itself to the colloid. The known result is that the new combination is insoluble in water or at least much less soluble than the original mixture. It is this reaction to light that makes bichromated colloids so important to platemaking in all graphic arts processes. The results of LTF's studies on this subject are published in its Bulletin No. 218, *The Light-Sensitivity of Bichromated Colloids*.

VARIABLES

While we don't know all the chemistry of the light-hardening process, it has been possible to study it and learn enough about it to control it. Before this work was done, lithographers didn't know what was causing variations so they couldn't possibly avoid them. Obviously, most of the trouble was due to unexpected changes in light sensitivity of the dried plate coatings which caused the coatings on successive plates to be hardened to different degrees by the same light exposure. So let's discuss the things that can affect the light sensitivity of the bichromated gum deep-etch coating, and how they can be controlled so the platemaker can be sure of uniformly good results in day-to-day production.

The things that have to be controlled in order to produce deep-etch coatings of the same light sensitivity at all times are:

1. Bichromate-gum ratio in the coating solution.
2. pH (alkalinity) of the coating.
3. Coating thickness.
4. Age of the dried coating.
5. Temperature.
6. Relative humidity.

These are called variables because each one can vary. Changes in the first three can be made either intentionally or accidentally by the platemaker. The fourth often depends on the nature of the job—in other words, the length of time it takes to complete the light exposure and start the development. The last two are continually changing in most shops, but can be kept practically constant by air conditioning. The following discussion tells how these variables affect the light sensitivity of deep-etch coatings and what the lithographer can do to control them or prevent their bad effects.

BICHROMATE-GUM RATIO. The light sensitivity of the deep-etch coating increases as the ratio of ammonium bichromate to gum arabic in its formula (Chapter 7, page 61) is increased. In other words, if you should increase the amount of bichromate without increasing the gum arabic, your coatings would be more light sensitive. If you should decrease the bichromate, they would be less light sensitive. In either case your regular light exposure would produce a different degree of hardening than with correctly made coatings.

In the LTF deep-etch coating solution formula (Chapter 7, page 61), the bichromate-gum ratio is 1:4.18 (one part of dry ammonium bichromate to 4.18 parts of dry gum arabic by

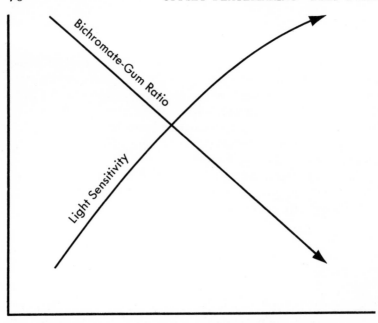

Figure 29. As the bichromate-gum ratio of the coating decreases, its light sensitivity increases.

weight). In commercial deep-etch coating solutions this ratio is probably between 1:3 and 1:5 and will depend on the brand. If you use a commercial deep-etch coating and should change from one brand to another, you may find that you need a slightly different light exposure since the new brand may have a different bichromate-gum ratio.

pH (ALKALINITY) OF THE COATING. As mentioned in Chapter 7, deep-etch coatings contain ammonium hydroxide in addition to ammonium bichromate and gum arabic. The reason for this is that the bichromate-gum mixture alone is acid and unstable. It becomes useless after a few hours. But if it is made alkaline with ammonia, it will keep for months. The LTF deep-etch coating solution has a pH value of 8.8 to 9.0. If you prepare it yourself, you should check its pH value to be sure it is correct (see Chapter 2, page 15). Most commercial deep-etch coating solutions have pH values in the range 8.5 to 9.5. You shouldn't have to check them since they are made with laboratory control.

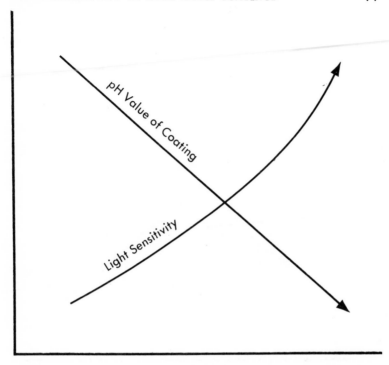

Figure 30. As the pH value of the coating is decreased, its light sensitivity increases.

The amount of ammonia in the coating solution has an effect on the light sensitivity of plate coatings. Most of this ammonia evaporates within a half hour or so after the coating has dried. But the amount that remains in the coating at any given time depends on the original pH of the coating solution. The more there is, the less light sensitive the coating will be. This is the reason why it is important to have the pH value of the coating solution the same at all times.

COATING THICKNESS. Thick coatings require longer exposure than thin coatings. This is because light hardens them from the top down. The thicker the coating, the longer it takes the light to harden it right down to the metal surface so it will adhere and can be developed properly. The effect of changing the coating thickness is therefore the same as that of changing its light sensitivity.

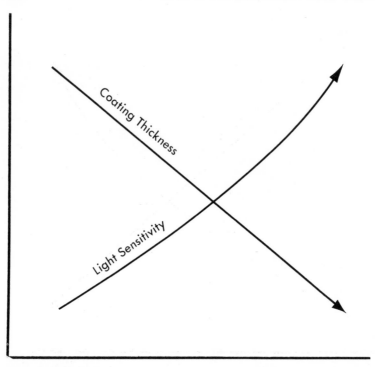

Figure 31. The thinner the deep-etch coating, the greater is its light sensitivity.

Keeping the coating thickness constant from plate to plate is very important. To do this you have to keep the following things constant:

1. Plate grain
2. Solids content of the coating solution
3. Viscosity of the coating solution
4. Temperature
5. Amount of moisture on the plate when the coating solution is applied
6. Volume of coating solution used on each size of plate
7. Relative humidity
8. Whirler speed

The *plate grain* must be the same from plate to plate. If you coat a coarse-grained plate and a fine-grained plate, using the same coating solution and keeping all the other things that affect coating thickness the same, the coatings will not be equally thick. If the coating is the proper thickness for the fine-grained plate, it will be too thin for the coarse-grained plate. This is because the higher peaks of the coarse grain will be covered so thinly that the light-hardened coating may be penetrated by the developer and deep-etching solutions. This would produce a scummy plate. Conversely, if the coating is thick enough for the coarse-grained plate, it will be too thick for the fine-grained plate.

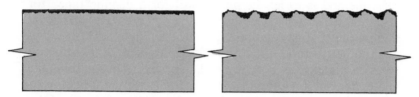

Figure 32. This shows the same amount of coating on coarse- and fine-grained plates. The peaks of the coarse grain are not well covered.

The *solids content* of the coating solution is the amount of dry solids (ammonium bichromate plus gum arabic) in a gallon of the solution. As long as you use the same coating solution formula, the solids content will be the same. Any one brand of commercial coating solution should always have the same solids content. The best way to check this is to test coating solutions with a Baumé hydrometer (see Chapter 2, page 14).

Viscosity or pouring thickness of the coating solution may vary with different lots of gum arabic. If you make your own coating solution, you can't control its viscosity very well unless you have a viscometer with constant temperature control and are able to select or blend your gum arabic. Commercial coating solutions, being made under laboratory control, should be fairly constant in viscosity.

The viscosity of the coating solution changes with *temperature*. The higher the temperature, the thinner or more fluid the solution is, and vice versa. So, to get coatings of uniform thickness from plate to plate, the temperature of both the plate and the coating solution should be as nearly constant as possible. This is why the plate should be flushed with a large amount of water at 85° or 90° F. just before you coat it (see Chapter 7, page 61 and 65). It is also the reason for keeping the coating solution at room temperature and not in a refrigerator.

The *amount of moisture on the plate* when you pour on the coating solution affects the final coating thickness. This moisture dilutes or thins the solution. The more moisture there is, the thinner the final coating will be. The plate must, of course, carry some moisture. A dry plate isn't wet instantly by the coating solution and is very difficult to coat. To be sure there is always the same amount of moisture on your plates, the best method is to let the plate whirl for a definite time (for example, 30 seconds) between shutting off the water and pouring on the coating solution (see Chapter 7, page 62).

Another method of controlling the amount of moisture on grained plates is used by some platemakers. After flushing the plate, they let it whirl and watch the reflection of a light from the wet surface. When this reflection loses its sharpness and the surface becomes dull or satiny, they apply the coating solution.

The *volume of coating solution* used on a plate affects the coating thickness. More than the right amount of solution gives a thicker coating because it is diluted less by the moisture on the plate. Likewise, less than the right amount of solution produces a thinner coating.

The higher the *relative humidity* the slower the coating will dry. So, everything else being the same, more of the solution will be whirled off the plate on humid days than on dry days. High humidity therefore produces thin coatings and low humidity, thick coatings. If you don't have air conditioning to keep the temperature and humidity constant in your plate room, you may have to slow down the whirler on humid days and speed it up on dry days.

If all the above things are held constant, the *whirler speed* controls the thickness of the dried coating. As you coat a plate, you notice that its rotation makes the coating solution flow from the center to the edges where the excess is thrown off. The force that causes this flow is called "Centrifugal Force". It increases as the speed of rotation increases. The faster the plate is whirled, the more coating solution reaches the edges and is thrown off before it dries enough to stop flowing. So, the faster the whirler speed, the thinner the final dried coating will be, and vice versa.

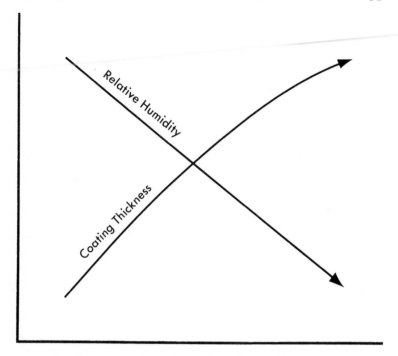

Figure 33. At the same whirler speed, the coating thickness increases as the relative humidity decreases.

If all the other factors that can affect coating thickness remained unchanged from plate to plate, the whirler speed would never have to be changed. This refers, of course, to the final whirling speed after you have poured all the coating solution onto the plate. But if one or more of them changes in such a way as to produce a thicker coating, you can easily counteract its effect by speeding up the whirler. If the change would produce a thinner coating, you can slow down the whirler. This is the main reason why modern whirlers are equipped with variable speed drives.

The reason for all this discussion of coating thickness is to emphasize the importance of keeping the various things that affect it constant. But usually you don't have to worry about solids content and viscosity of the coating solution. And you can control all the other things except relative humidity pretty well by the methods outlined. While relative humidity can vary

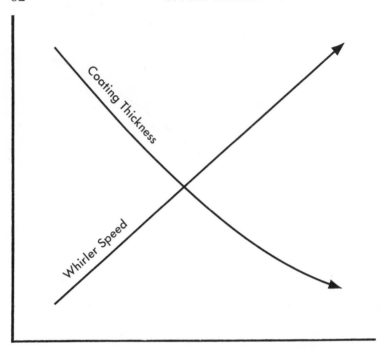

Figure 34. The higher the whirler speed, the thinner the coating.

greatly in non-air-conditioned shops, its effect on coating thickness is not too great if you use heat in the whirler.

The most important thing in coating plates is to perform the sequence of steps always in the same way. Then, if you find that the coating is too thick or too thin, you can make a correction on your next plate. Usually, the simplest way to do this is to change the whirler speed.

How do you tell whether the coating is too thick or too thin? On grained plates you can often tell by the appearance of the dried coating. The thicker the coating is the glossier or shinier it will appear. You will soon learn by experience the degree of glossiness to look for.

Variations in coating thickness will, of course, show up after the plate has been exposed and developed. By watching the development carefully you can tell whether it is normal. If it isn't normal, you should make the indicated adjustment, usually a change in whirler speed, when you coat the next plate.

AGE OF THE DRIED COATING. The freshly dried coating doesn't have its maximum light sensitivity. This is partly because it loses its ammonia rather slowly. And, until the ammonia is gone, the coating is constantly becoming more light sensitive. After the dried plate is removed from the whirler, it takes about half an hour for the coating to lose enough of its ammonia for its light sensitivity to become reasonably constant.

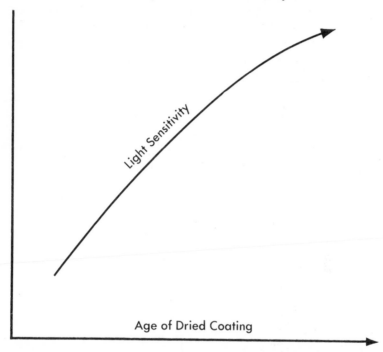

Figure 35. The longer the dried coating stands before the plate is exposed, the greater will be its light sensitivity.

Except when the relative humidity is above 70 per cent, a good rule is to allow a half hour after you take the plate from the whirler before starting the exposure. This insures not only the loss of residual ammonia, but also that the plate will have cooled to room temperature, and the coating will have come into balance with the relative humidity of the room atmosphere. All these things are necessary for uniform light sensitivity at the time the plate is to be exposed.

The next question is, how long can the coated plate be kept before the entire coating becomes too insoluble to be developed? The answer is, this depends on the temperature and relative humidity.

Just as soon as the plate coating has dried it begins to harden, even without the action of light. This spontaneous hardening is called "dark reaction". It is, of course, much slower than the hardening produced by light. But, if it goes too far, the entire coating becomes insoluble. If you exposed such a plate to light, you wouldn't be able to develop an image, at least not completely enough to make a good plate. Whether the plate ages before or after the exposures makes little difference.

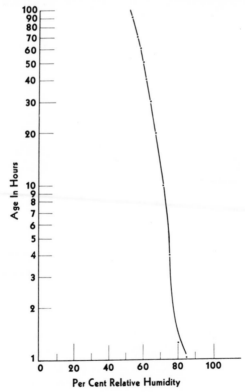

Figure 36. This curve shows the time required for deep-etch coatings on plates to reach the same degree of hardness or insolubility due to dark reaction at different relative humidities when the temperature is 78° F.

This dark reaction is faster the higher the temperature and relative humidity. Figure 36 shows about how long a plate will keep in good condition at 78° F. after it has been coated—in other words, the length of time you can take to expose it and still be able to develop it properly. At higher temperatures the time will be somewhat shorter, and at lower temperatures, somewhat longer. When the relative humidity is below 50 per cent and the temperature no higher than 80° F., you can keep coated plates as long as three or four days before you have to develop them. When the relative humidity is 70 per cent, a plate has to be developed within six to eight hours in order to produce a satisfactory image. If the relative humidity should go as high as 80 per cent, this time would be cut to between one and two hours.

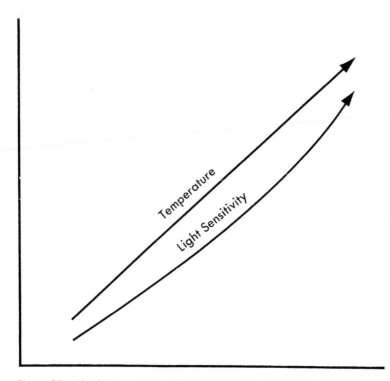

Figure 37. The light sensitivity of the dried coating becomes greater as the temperature increases.

TEMPERATURE. The light sensitivity of the dried coating is greater the higher the temperature. And, as we said before, the dark reaction is also faster. Therefore, the dry plate coating should be protected as much as possible from temperatures higher than room temperature. The greatest damage from high temperature comes from leaving plates in a heated whirler after the coating is dry. It is a good idea to set an alarm clock just after the plate has been coated, when you close the whirler and turn on the heat. By checking a few plates to see how long it takes them to dry, you can find out just the length of time necessary. When the alarm rings, take the plate from the whirler immediately.

RELATIVE HUMIDITY. The light sensitivity of the dried coating is greater the higher the relative humidity. And the dark reaction is also faster. Therefore, in non-air conditioned shops where the relative humidity is continually changing, the light sensitivity of coatings is bound to be different from plate to plate. You can get coatings of uniform light sensitivity only if the platemaking room is air conditioned.

If your shop has no air conditioning, the best thing you can do is to adjust the light exposure or coating thickness to compensate (make allowance) for changes in relative humidity. The first requirement for this is to have an accurate hygrometer (see Chapter 2, page 17) and to know how to use it. You can then check the relative humidity each time you are ready to coat a plate. If it has gone up since you made your last plate, shorten the exposure. If it has gone down, lengthen the exposure accordingly. If the change in relative humidity is 20% or more, changing the exposure is not enough. In this case, the coating thickness must be changed.

UNIMPORTANT FACTORS. The following things have little or no effect on the light sensitivity of deep-etch coatings:

1. The *plate metal*. Whether the plate is zinc, aluminum or stainless steel makes no noticeable difference, provided the grain and all other factors are the same.

2. *Surface treatments*. Cronaking zinc plates or Brunaking aluminum plates has no noticeable effect on the light sensitivity of coatings.

3. *Color of the coating solution*. Some commercial deep-etch

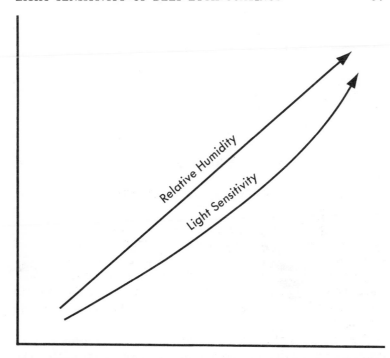

Figure 38. When the relative humidity goes up, the light sensitivity of the dried coating increases.

coating solutions contain a dye, usually blue, that gives them a green color. Careful checks show that this color has little or no effect on the coating's light sensitivity.

COATINGS ON UNGRAINED PLATES

All that we have said in this chapter about the light sensitivity of deep-etch coatings on grained plates applies equally to coatings on ungrained and brush-grained plates. It is just as important that all the factors listed on page 75 which affect the coating's light sensitivity be kept constant. The things that are most likely to vary, of course, are temperature and relative humidity. Any effects such changes may have on coating thickness can be corrected for by changing the whirler speed. And if the coating thickness can be kept reasonably constant, variations in light sensitivity can be corrected for by making the proper adjustment in the light exposure.

Chapter 9

EXPOSING THE PLATE

In our discussion we are now at the point where we have the plate coated, dried and ready to be exposed. Under normal conditions, that is, if the relative humidity is below 70 per cent, the plate will have been out of the whirler for about 30 minutes. Its coating will have lost most of its ammonia and will have cooled and come to balance with the room's relative humidity.

The purpose of the light exposure is to harden the bichromated gum coating on the non-image areas of the plate. The unhardened coating on the image areas can then be removed by development leaving only bare metal in these areas.

MATERIALS AND EQUIPMENT FOR THE EXPOSURE

In order to make good deep-etch plates the first requirement is *good positives*. Positives, of course, are photographic transparencies in which the image areas are opaque (black) and the non-image areas are transparent (clear). They are made in the camera room from original negatives of the job to be printed. By good positives we mean positives in which (1) the lines, solids, and halftone dots are opaque, free from pinholes, and have sharp edges free from fuzziness or haloes, (2) the transparent portions are free from fog and dirt specks. There are a number of LTF publications that deal with the production of positives for deep-etch*.

---

*LTF Publications on Photography are:
   No. 503, *Offset Photography (Line)*
   No. 508, *Offset Photography (Halftone)*
   No. 510, *Tone and Color Correcting (Dot Etching)*
   No. 511, *Tone and Color Correcting (Hand Retouching)*

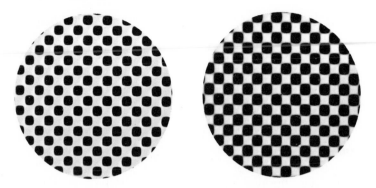

Figure 39. These are photomicrographs of good and bad halftone positives. The one on the left is satisfactory, while the one on the right is too soft and fuzzy.

In planning the layout for a deep-etch plate it is important, whenever possible, to include one or more LTF Sensitivity Guides. These are continuous-tone grey scales about half an inch wide and five inches long. They contain 21 steps of increasing density or opacity which are numbered, starting with No. 1 at the transparent end. The Sensitivity Guide images produced on the plate make it possible for the platemaker to control both the light exposure and the development of deep-etch plates. For the details on making and using LTF Sensitivity Guides, see LTF Bulletin No. 215, *The Sensitivity Guide.*

The equipment used in exposing the plate depends largely on the nature of the job to be printed. If it is a black and white job, a simple color job that doesn't require close register, or

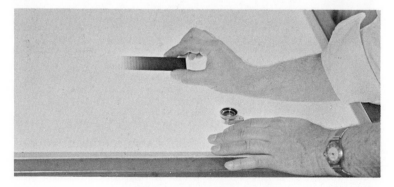

Figure 40. The LTF Sensitivity Guide.

if there are only one or two subjects to go on the plate, the exposure may be made in a vacuum printing frame. But, if it is a color job that requires close register, and particularly if there are to be a number of subjects—either the same or different—on the plate, a photo-composing machine is generally used.

*   *   *   *

The *vacuum printing frame consists* of two wooden or metal frames, one of which carries a corrugated or channeled rubber blanket, and the other a sheet of flawless plate glass. In the smaller sizes the two frames are generally hinged together on one side. The rubber blanket is connected to a vacuum pump by means of a flexible rubber tube.

Figure 41. The coated plate is being exposed in a vacuum printing frame. Note the Sensitivity Guide at the bottom of the positive.

When the printing frame is open, the blanket frame is horizontal and the glass is raised up out of the way. The sensitized metal plate is laid on the blanket, coated side up. The positive, or a "flat" consisting of film with several positives stripped onto it (see LTF Bulletin No. 507, "Offset Stripping (Black and White)"), is laid on the plate in position, emulsion side down. The glass frame is lowered and the two frames are locked together. The vacuum pump is then turned on. It sucks the air from between the blanket and glass, thus forcing the sensitized plate and positive into very close contact. When this has been done, the printing frame is turned to a vertical position facing an arc lamp which, when turned on, gives the necessary exposure.

The non-image areas of the flat must be entirely transparent so that the plate coating will be uniformly hardened in these areas to form the "deep-etch stencil". However, if the plate is to receive two or more exposures using the same positive, parts of the plate to be used for the succeeding exposures must be protected from light with black or goldenrod paper. And during the succeeding exposures, areas already exposed must be masked out. When this masking is done, there are usually margins that receive no light exposure at all. Stopping-out to prevent these margins from printing will be discussed in a later chapter.

*   *   *   *

A *photo-composing machine* is a device for producing a series of exposures on the same plate, using the same or different subjects. There are two general types: one in which the plate is held stationary and the subject or positive is moved both horizontally and vertically, and the other in which the plate is moved horizontally and the positive is moved vertically. In either case the movement is made by means of lead screws. Accurate positioning for the exposures is obtained by various methods depending on the make or model of the machine.

The sensitized plate is placed on the bed in a predetermined position and held by means of adhesive tape.

The subject, consisting of one or more positives stripped on plate glass, is registered in a chase or positive holder. This is placed in the positive carriage of the machine. Vacuum is used to obtain close contact between positive and plate during each exposure to the arc light. The photo-composing machine thus is capable of accurately positioning a series of exposures on a plate, and of duplicating exposures in accurate register on a series of color plates.

When the plate is on the photo-composing machine, all areas except that opposite the chase opening are protected from light. Many subjects, however, don't occupy all of the

Figure 42. One type of photocomposing machine, showing the plate mounted and ready to be lifted to the vertical position in contact with the positive. The arc lamp is shown at right.

chase opening, and the unoccupied areas of the glass must be masked to prevent exposures from overlapping adjacent images. This masking is preferably done with thin aluminum foil. Wherever possible, the exposures are made to overlap a little so that the borders receive double exposure and are protected during the development and deep-etching. If this can't be done, the unexposed borders can be prevented from becoming printing areas in two ways:

1. By masking the exposed work areas with foil or goldenrod paper and giving the unexposed borders a separate exposure to an arc light to harden them.

2. By stopping out the unexposed borders with shellac or lacquer before the development, or with deep-etch coating solution just after the plate has been deep-etched. Stopping-out will be discussed in a later chapter.

For a detailed discussion of photo-composing machines and their operation, see LTF Bulletin No. 515, "Photo-Composing".

*   *   *   *

With both printing frames and photo-composing machines, light for the exposure is supplied by a powerful *arc lamp* using "photographic daylight" carbons. There are two general types. In the older type the gap between the carbons, or length of

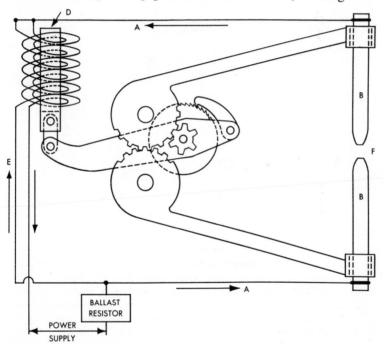

Figure 43a. Diagram of solenoid-controlled arc lamp. The current A that flows through the carbons B also flows through one coil of the solenoid C and generates magnetism that lifts the core D causing the carbons to separate and the arc to light. However, some current E is shunted around the arc and goes through another coil of the solenoid C that is wound oppositely to the first coil, generating an opposing magnetism. As the carbons burn and the gap F gets longer, less current flows through the arc and more flows through the shunt. The magnetism that lifts the core D becomes weaker, allowing the carbons to come closer together.

the arc light, is controlled by an electromagnet or solenoid. As the carbons burn, the gap becomes longer. At a certain point the solenoid acts to shorten the gap and holds the carbons in the new position until the gap again reaches its maximum length. This intermittent adjustment of the carbons causes a periodic variation in the light intensity.

Motor-driven arcs were introduced in 1947 to overcome this variation in light intensity. An electric motor feeds the carbons as they burn so that the length of the gap is maintained nearly constant. The light from motor-driven arcs is much more constant than that from the older types.

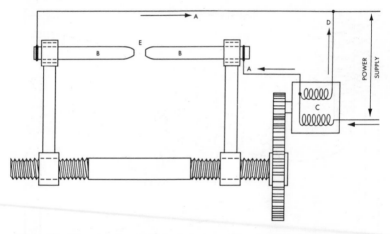

Figure 43b. Diagram of motor-driven arc lamp. The current A that flows through the carbons B also flows through one field coil of the motor C and drives it in the direction that separates the carbons and causes the arc to light. However, some current D is shunted around the arc and goes through another field coil in the motor C that generates an opposing field. As the carbons burn and the gap E gets longer, less current flows through the arc and more flows through the shunt. When the current D gets strong enough, it drives the motor in the opposite direction and feeds the carbons just fast enough to keep E constant.

Integrating light meters for controlling exposures in platemaking were introduced just after World War II. They measure the exposure in terms of light units reaching the plate regardless of light intensity, just as a water meter measures water in cubic feet regardless of its rate of flow. With solenoid-controlled arcs it was found that, when exposures were timed by

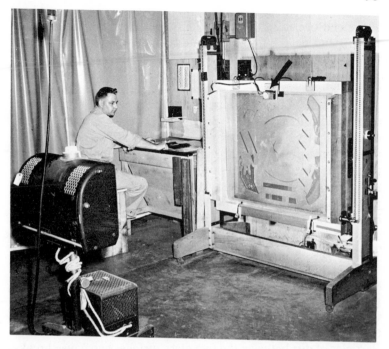

Figure 44. This shows an integrating light meter controlling an exposure in a vacuum printing frame. The arrow indicates the photo-cell, and the control box is mounted on the wall at the rear.

the clock, the amount of exposure received by the plate coating could vary as much as 25 per cent. The use of integrating light meters has prevented this variation. Motor-driven arcs, however, give such a steady light that the need for integrating light meters with them is questionable.

METHOD OF EXPOSING DEEP-ETCH PLATES

With the plate in proper contact with the positive in the printing frame, set the timer or integrating light meter for the desired exposure, turn on the arc, and then turn it off when the exposure is completed. The same is done, of course, on the photo-composing machine, except that it is repeated the necessary number of times using either the same or different positives in their predetermined positions on the plate. Most photo-composing machines can be set to turn off the arc automatically at the end of each exposure. The proper exposure in any case will depend on a number of conditions which will be covered in the following discussion.

Discussion

The amount of *vacuum* used to produce contact between the plate and positive can vary considerably. Most vacuum pumps can pull up to 28 inches of vacuum which corresponds to 13.7 pounds pressure per square inch or 1975 pounds per square foot. This amount of pressure is not needed. And if you are using glass positives, or heavy gauge plates, the strain on the glass might be enough to break it. High vacuum can also emboss thin metal plates. Most platemakers, therefore, use from 10 to 15 inches of vacuum (700 to 1060 lbs. per square foot). They secure the vacuum they want by adjusting a relief valve.

Even with the lower vaccum, certain precautions are necessary to prevent embossing of plates and possible breakage of glass positives or of the plate glass in the printing frame. If you use a glass positive in a vacuum printing frame, be sure that the positive and the printing frame glass are absolutely clean. Particles of dirt between the two glass surfaces can cause breakage. And if the glass positive is smaller than the plate, be sure to place strips of cardboard around the positive to support the edges of the plate and keep them from bending when the vacuum is turned on. For precautions in handling positives on photo-composing machines, see LTF Bulletin No. 515, "Photo-Composing", Chapter 10.

Keep the vacuum constant from plate to plate. If the vacuum is changed, this may change the light sensitivity of the plate coating.   *   *   *   *

The vacuum gauge is mounted somewhere in the vacuum line between the printing frame or chase and the pump. It indicates the vacuum at its connection. It doesn't necessarily measure the vacuum at all points in the area to be exposed. If there are leaks in the printing frame or chase gaskets, the vacuum in at least part of the exposure area could be somewhat lower than the gauge indicates. To avoid such leaks the system should be checked frequently.

One way to test for leaks is to check the contact between the

Figure 45. Checking the contact between positive and plate in a vacuum printing frame.

positive and a plate with the vacuum on. Hold a magnifying glass on an image area, preferably a halftone, and illuminate the area with a pen flashlight held at a 45° angle. If you have sufficient vacuum for good contact, you will see only one sharp image. If the image on the positive throws a shadow, or appears blurred, there is not enough vacuum for good contact.

Another way to check for leaks is to find how well the printing frame or chase holds vacuum after you turn off the vacuum pump. In many cases there is a check valve in the vacuum line that prevents air from re-entering after the vacuum pump is turned off. In some cases there is automatic control of the vacuum and the pump operates intermittently. In any case, the printing frame or chase, once evacuated, should be tight enough so that the gauge indicates only a very slow drop in vacuum.

A leaky chase gasket can produce a scummy plate. Dry air sucked between the gasket and the plate can cause severe local drying of the plate coating. This can result in checking or cracking of the coating so that it is penetrated by the developer and deep-etching solution later on.

*   *   *   *

A *single-arc lamp* is best for exposing the plate. Multiple arc lamps or banks of fluorescent lights tend to cause "undercutting" of the positive image, especially if the contact between positive and plate is not perfect. This sharpens halftones (reduces halftone values) and causes the loss of fine highlight dots. Most printing lamps today are single arc.

In exposing the plate it is important to get nearly uniform light coverage. To do this the arc should be about as far away from the plate as the length of the diagonal of the area to be

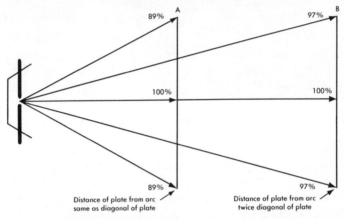

Figure 46. This diagram shows how light intensity on the plate during exposure falls off from center to corners. At position A the fall-off is 11%. At position B it is only 3%. But the exposure at position B would have to be four times as long as at A.

exposed. In a printing frame, this is usually the diagonal of the plate. On a photo-composing machine it is the diagonal of the chase opening. The farther away the light is, the more even the illumination on the plate will be. But since the exposure time increases as the square of the distance between the light and the plate, we have to sacrifice some uniformity of light coverage to avoid excessively long exposures.

*   *   *   *

LTF Sensitivity Guides can be purchased ready-made (see page 89) or you can make them yourself. Simply buy some No. 2 Photographic Step Tablets from Eastman Kodak Co. Cut each tablet in half to make two strips about half an inch wide. Number the strips in india ink starting with "1" at the transparent end and ending with "21" at the opaque end.

Wherever possible include one or more Sensitivity Guides in the work to be printed on the plate. Just what you can do will depend on free space in the layout. Usually there are margins or open spaces where you can insert the Guide. On photo-composed plates it is often impossible to include a Sensitivity Guide as part of the work in each exposure. In this case it can be shot (exposed) in separately, after the work exposures have been completed. Care should be taken to give the Guide exactly the same exposure as the regular work areas. The images of the Sensitivity Guide on the plate can be staged or polished out after they have served their purpose. But, whenever possible, they should be left on the plate since they are a help to the pressman in controlling the quality of printing.

The value of the LTF Sensitivity Guide lies in the fact that

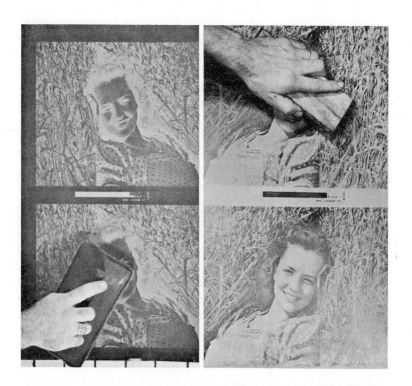

Figure 47. LTF Sensitivity Guide

it gives a series of increasing exposures of the coating. After normal development, the highest numbered Guide step not laid bare shows the degree of hardening of the stencil produced by the exposure. In deep-etch platemaking this step will be in the range "5" to "8". If it is higher than "8", the stencil is over-exposed. If lower than "5", it is under-exposed. Sensitivity Guides vary somewhat in density, so that with different guides the steps indicating correct exposure may be different. So each platemaker must find by trial the exposure that, with his positives and normal development, will give the tone values he wants. This will produce a definite Guide step. Then, by always exposing and developing plates to produce this same step, he will get uniform results. For further information on the use of LTF Sensitivity Guides, see LTF Bulletin No. 215, *The Sensitivity Guide.*

                   *   *   *   *

Air conditioning is a great help in platemaking as we stated in Chapter 8. If your plate room is air conditioned, the temperature should not vary more than 5°F (70-75° or 75-80°). Also the relative humidity (RH) should not be higher than 50 per cent and should not vary more than 5 per cent (for example, 45-50 per cent). Under these conditions you shouldn't have to change anything in your coating and exposing procedure to compensate for atmospheric changes. Just use the Sensitivity Guide to be sure that all the other factors affecting the coating's light sensitivity are kept in line (see Chapter 8).

If your plate room is not air conditioned, the making of uniformly good plates becomes complicated. You will have to correct for the effects of changing temperature and relative humidity on coating thickness (Chapter 8, page 77). You will also have to change the light exposure to compensate for the effects of temperature and relative humidity on the coating's light sensitivity (Chapter 8, page 86). Since there are no sure ways of telling exactly how much correction to make in any case, you have to use a good deal of care and judgment. You will have to know what changes in temperature and relative humidity have taken place. You will have to estimate and make adjustments in your coating procedure and exposure to compensate for the changes. You will have to watch the development of the Sensitivity Guide image to see if your adjust-

ments were just right, too small, or too great, and make further
adjustments on your next plate accordingly. This requires more
care and experience, and the results are not as sure as in an
air conditioned plateroom.

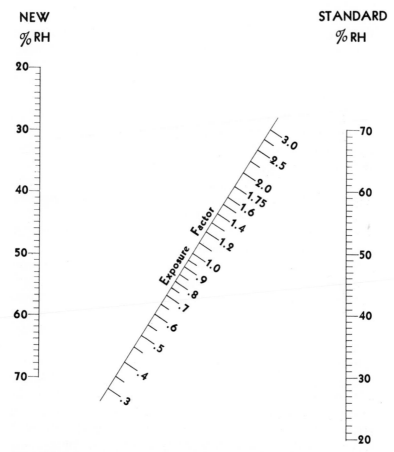

Figure 48. Exposure chart for estimating changes in exposure for known changes
in relative humidity. For use, see example in text.

EXPOSURE CHART. To help the platemaker, LTF has worked
out an exposure chart that he can use in estimating how much
he should change the exposure for any change in relative humidity. The following is an example of how to use this chart:

Example

Let's say that you have made a satisfactory plate at 50 per cent relative humidity and 75° F. with a three-minute light exposure. But, when you are ready to make your next plate, the relative humidity has gone up to 62 per cent. To find the new exposure, lay a ruler on the chart crossing the "Standard RH" line at 50 per cent and the "New RH" line at 62 per cent. Note that the ruler crosses the diagonal "Exposure Factor" line at 0.7. Then, multiplying 3 minutes by 0.7 gives 2.1 minutes or 2 minutes and 6 seconds for your new exposure at 62 per cent RH.

LIMITATIONS OF THE EXPOSURE CHART. The exposure chart should not be depended upon alone if the RH has changed as much as 20 per cent, or more. Such a large change will have affected the coating thickness too much (see Chapter 8, page 86). If the RH rises 20 per cent or more, decrease your whirler speed. If the RH drops 20 per cent or more, increase your whirler speed or lower the Baumé of your coating solution one or two degrees by adding a little water. These changes will tend to keep the coating thickness uniform.

The exposure chart shows only the changes in exposure needed to compensate for changes in relative humidity. It can't take into account the effects of changes in temperature, thickness of the coating, and dark reaction. Its figures are based on the same coating thickness and one to three hours between coating and development. So it is only a rough guide. The Sensitivity Guide will show you how close the chart's predictions are to being correct, and then it is up to you to make the final adjustments in exposure on succeeding plates.

Every platemaking department should have a thermometer and a hygrometer. If you have a wet-and-dry-bulb hygrometer, its dry-bulb thermometer will give you the room temperature. If you have a direct-reading hygrometer, you will need a separate thermometer. For a further discussion of hygrometers, review Chapter 2, pages 17 to 21.

*   *   *   *

When a plate is photo-composed, it may have to be on the machine as long as eight hours. If the exposure isn't finished during one shift, the plate may have to stay in the machine overnight. During all this time "dark reaction" will be hardening the coating (see Chapter 8, page 84). If the temperature and relative humidity are low, the extra time may not cause any trouble. But if they are high, the coating will harden overnight so much that the image can't be developed. The dark reaction curve in Chapter 8, page 84, will show you about how long a plate can be held on the photo-composing machine before the coating will fail to develop properly.

There is another kind of hardening of the coating that takes place without light. After each exposure, the exposed coating continues to harden still further. This is called "continuing reaction". It is not serious if your positives are dense and the dots are sharp. But, if positives are gray or if the dots are "fuzzy edged", the continuing reaction will cause dots and lines to sharpen. This action is also faster at high temperatures and humidities.

This discussion of dark and continuing reactions is to show you the importance of exposing and developing plates as quickly as possible after they have been coated and allowed to cool to room temperature, especially in hot, humid weather. The big advantage of air conditioning is that it eliminates temperature and humidity variations and most of the troubles that go with them.

For a more complete discussion of dark reaction and continuing reaction, see LTF Bulletin No. 218, "The Sensitivity of Bichromated Colloids".

Chapter 10

DEVELOPING THE PLATE

Our plate has now been exposed and is ready to be developed. At this point, it may be desirable to stop out unexposed margins or other areas that should not print. Stopping-out can be done either before developing or after deep-etching the plate, depending on circumstances. Rather than divide this subject, both methods of stopping-out will be discussed in Chapter 13.

The purpose of development is to remove the unhardened bichromated-gum coating from the image areas of the plate in preparation for deep-etching these areas.

THE DEEP-ETCH DEVELOPER

Development of the exposed deep-etch coating requires a special developing solution. Water can't be used because it dissolves the hardened as well as the unhardened parts. To secure proper development we must use a strong salt solution that contains a weak acid. For more about the chemistry of deep-etch developers, see LTF Bulletin 401, "Chemistry of Lithography".

There are a number of good commercial deep-etch developers. Generally these are designed to work best with the same brand of deep-etch coating, but all are similar in their action. If you prefer to make your own developer, LTF recommends the following two formulas:

Regular Developer

	Metric Units	U. S. Units
Calcium Chloride Solution, 40-41° Bé	1000 cc.	1 gallon
Lactic Acid, 85%	53 cc.	6¾ liq. oz. (200 cc.)

Stabilized Developer

	Metric Units	U. S. Units
Water	1000 cc.	2 quarts
Zinc Chloride (ZnCl$_2$), Technical	350 g.	1½ lbs.
Calcium Chloride (CaCl$_2$ · 2H$_2$O), Commercial	700 g.	3 lbs.
Lactic Acid, 85%	160 cc.	11½ liq. oz. (340 cc.)

Instructions for making the 40-41° Baumé calcium chloride solution, and for preparing and testing the developers, are given in the Appendix.

The same deep-etch developer is used on zinc plates, aluminum plates, and stainless steel plates, whether grained or ungrained. But the method of development varies somewhat.

METHOD OF DEVELOPING GRAINED ZINC PLATES

To develop the exposed plate, first place it in the deep-etching sink. Pour a generous supply of developer on the plate and work it evenly over the entire surface with a deep-etch developing pad (a plush-covered wooden block) using moderate pressure. Within two to three minutes the image areas should clear and begin to froth. Watch particularly the Sensitivity Guide images and stop the development as soon as step 8 has cleared. (It may be that you will want step 7 to clear instead of step 8. Individual guides vary somewhat and you will have to find this out by experience.) By the time step 8 has cleared, the frothing will have reached step 9.

Squeegee off the spent developer and pour on a fresh supply. Work this over the plate for two to three minutes. If step 6 doesn't froth within three minutes, squeegee the developer off and apply it a third time. Continue rubbing with the developing pad until step 6 froths.

When the final application of developer has been squeegeed off, the image areas are ready to be deep-etched.

In developing plates on which the Sensitivity Guide couldn't be used, you have only the action of the developer on the

Figure 49. Developing a deep-etch plate.

image areas to guide you. They should clear and begin to froth within two to three minutes with the first application of developer. At this point squeegee off the spent developer. Make a second application, work it over the plate for the same length of time as the first development, and squeegee it off. Make still a third application of developer, also for the same length of time. Normally, the three applications should take a total of six to nine minutes.

When the third application of developer has been squeegeed off, the plate is ready to be deep-etched.

METHOD OF DEVELOPING GRAINED ALUMINUM PLATES

The difference between zinc and aluminum plates in development is that aluminum doesn't froth when the image areas clear. It is attacked very little by the lactic acid in the developer. The only difference this makes in the development of aluminum plates is that the platemaker must judge by the clearing alone.

In developing aluminum plates, work the first application of developer over the plate until the image areas clear, and squeegee it off. This should take two to three minutes and the Sensitivity Guide image should clear to step 8 (or possibly 7).

Work the second application of developer over the plate for two to three minutes. If step 6 on the Sensitivity Guide image hasn't cleared after three minutes, squeegee the developer off and make a third application. Continue rubbing until step 6 clears.

When the third developer has been squeegeed off, the image areas are ready to be deep-etched.

In developing aluminum plates on which the Sensitivity Guide couldn't be used, you will have to judge the development by the appearance of the image areas alone. Here you should use the same system as for zinc plates that don't carry Sensitivity Guide images (see page 105). Of course there will be no frothing, but clearing of the image is easy to judge.

DEVELOPING GRAINED STAINLESS STEEL PLATES

The action of deep-etch developer on stainless steel is exactly the same as on aluminum. Simply follow the instructions given above for developing grained aluminum plates.

DEVELOPING UNGRAINED ZINC AND ALUMINUM PLATES

Ungrained and brush-grained plates carry a much thinner deep-etch coating than grained plates (see Chapter 7, page 64). And since their thinner coating is more light sensitive, the exposure to light produces a harder stencil covering the non-image areas. Because of the thin coating, one application of developer is all that is ever needed to prepare the image areas for deep-etching. Because of their harder stencil, development is not carried to as low a numbered step on the Sensitivity Guide image as is done in the case of grained plates.

To develop an ungrained zinc or aluminum plate, simply place it in the developing sink and pour on a generous supply of developer. Work the developer over the entire plate with the deep-etch developing pad.

If the plate is zinc, continue the development until step 9 of the Sensitivity Guide image begins to froth. If it is aluminum, develop until step 9 clears. In either case development should require not less than one and one-half minutes and not more than four minutes.

If there are no Sensitivity Guide images on the plate, develop until the image on zinc froths or the image on aluminum clears, then continue one half minute longer. This will give fairly good control, but use of the Sensitivity Guide is much better.

When development is complete, and the developer is squeegeed off, the plate is ready to be deep-etched.

Discussion

The deep-etching sink is a trough with a level grid or island in the center on which the plate is laid. The trough is somewhat larger than the largest plate to be developed. Since it is used for both development and deep-etching, the sink and its drain should be acid proof.

The grid or island should be one half to one inch smaller at each edge than the plate. This allows you to squeegee off spent developer or deep-etching solution without danger of dragging them back onto the plate. If you are making plates of different sizes, it is a good plan to have the grid the right size for your largest plates. Then, for smaller plates you can lay a piece of ¾ inch plywood of the proper size on the large grid to raise the plate up and prevent dragging back of spent solutions.

The deep-etch developing pad is a plush-covered wooden block. Use it for plate development only. And as soon as you have finished the development, rinse the pad thoroughly with

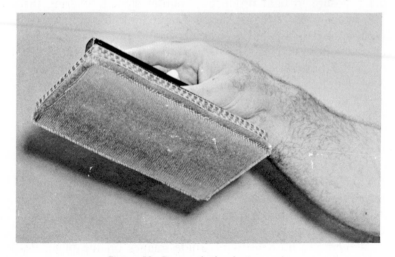

Figure 50. Deep-etch developing pad.

anhydrous alcohol, squeegee it as dry as possible, and stand it in a rack. At the end of the day or shift, wash the pad thoroughly with water, squeegee it as dry as possible, and let it dry overnight. The idea is not to let the pad stand with developer in it. The developer might pick up moisture from the air and damage your next plate.

*   *   *   *

There are four things that determine the time it takes you to develop a plate:
1. Thickness of the coating
2. Hardness of the unexposed coating in the image areas
3. Temperature
4. Baumé or density of the developer

In Chapter 8 we showed that thin coatings are more light sensitive than thick coatings, and emphasized the importance of keeping the coating thickness the same from plate to plate. Variations in coating thickness also affect the speed of development. Thin coatings on grained plates take longer to develop than thick coatings*. This may be because dark reaction hardens thin coatings faster in the unexposed image areas. It is another reason for trying to keep the coating thickness uniform from plate to plate.

If thickness of the coating is kept constant, its hardness in the image areas will depend on the amount of dark reaction that takes place between drying of the coating and starting the development. The longer this period is, the harder the unexposed coating will be. And since the dark reaction rate depends on temperature and relative humidity (Chapter 8, page 85), the hotter and more humid the weather, the harder the coating will become in the image areas.

If your platemaking room is air conditioned, the coating thickness, temperature and relative humidity variations should present no serious problem. The only variable you can't control is the time required for exposure. This will depend on the layout and on the number of shots the plate must be given on the photo-composing machine. But if your relative humidity is maintained at 50 per cent or lower, the dark reaction will be

*This statement doesn't apply to the relative time required to develop grained and ungrained plates. Ungrained plates carry such a thin coating that it develops more rapidly in spite of its greater hardness.

so slow that variations in photo-composing time will cause no trouble.

On the other hand, if your platemaking room is not air conditioned, you will have to expect variations in hardness of the unexposed coating in the image areas. And when the temperature and relative humidity are both high, the time between drying of the coating and starting the development may be limited to only a couple of hours (Chapter 8, page 85).

In any case there must be a distinct difference in hardness of the exposed non-image areas and unexposed image areas of the coating. Otherwise it won't be possible for the developer to dissolve the unexposed coating without also dissolving or penetrating the exposed coating.

This brings us to the factors of temperature and Baumé that affect the activity of the developer. Assuming that the plate has been exposed properly, and that there is enough difference in hardness between the exposed and unexposed coating to make proper development possible, the rate or speed of development will depend on the temperature and the Baumé of the developer.

Temperature strongly affects the speed of development. The higher the temperature the more rapidly development takes place, and vice versa. At high temperatures the action can be so rapid that you can't get uniform development, especially on large plates. At low temperatures it can be slow that it is hard to get complete development.

Some developers are affected more by temperature than others. The *regular developer* (page 105) is much more affected than the *stabilized developer*. Fortunately you can regulate the activity of the regular developer easily by adjusting its Baumé. The following table shows how this is done:

ADJUSTMENT OF REGULAR DEVELOPER
FOR DIFFERENT TEMPERATURES

| Room Temperature Degrees F. | Water to be added | | | Density of Adjusted Developer Degrees Baumé |
| | Per 1000 cc. of Developer cc. | Per gallon of Developer | | |
		Liq. oz.	cc.	
70-75	124	15¾	465	37
75-80	87	10½	340	38
80-85	42	5¼	155	39
Above 85	None	None	None	40

By adjusting the developer Baumé according to the room temperature you can keep the developing time nearly constant.

The stabilized developer works quite well from 68 to 90° F. While its speed of action increases somewhat as the temperature rises, you don't have to make any adjustment as long as you work in this range. But if you have to work at temperatures above 90° F., you can slow down the developer's action by adding about 26 ounces (770 cc.) of 51° Baumé zinc chloride to the gallon. This will raise its Baumé to 43 degrees. The 51° Baumé zinc chloride solution can be made as follows:

	Metric Units	U. S. Units
Zinc Chloride (ZnCl$_2$), Technical	920 g.	7¾ lbs.
Cold Water	1000 cc.	1 gallon

When dissolved, allow to cool to room temperature and test with a hydrometer. Add water, a little at a time, until the hydrometer shows 51° Baumé.

Most commercial deep-etch developers are similar to LTF's stabilized developer. If they should work too slow, they can be speeded up by adding enough water to lower their Baumé 1½ to 2 degrees. If, on the other hand, your commercial developer works too fast, ask the supplier what to do to slow it down.

* * * *

As we said in Chapter 8, the light sensitivity of the deep-etch coating becomes greater the higher the temperature and relative humidity. If only the humidity rises, you can correct for this by shortening the exposure. But if the temperature also rises, the developer becomes more active and you can't shorten the exposure very much unless you also increase the developer Baumé.

The best advice we can give is to follow the exposure chart (Chapter 9, page 101), as long as the temperature is between 70 and 80° F. If it goes above 80° F., feel your way along by watching how the Sensitivity Guide images develop. If the development becomes too rapid, raise the Baumé of the developer if possible. If not, increase your exposure so that the exposed areas of the coating will be harder and will resist the developer better.

If your coating thickness is right, you can tell two important things by watching both the regular image areas and the Sensitivity Guide images during the first development.

1. If the *regular image areas* start to clear in two to three minutes, the developer Baumé is correct. But if clearing takes less than two minutes or more than three minutes to start, the developer Baumé is not right and should be adjusted.

2. If *step 9 on the Sensitivity Guide* image starts to clear in from two to three minutes, your exposure is correct. But if the regular image areas start to clear in two to three minutes, while step 9 on the Sensitivity Guide image takes longer than three minutes to clear, the exposure is too long and should be shortened on subsequent plates. On the other hand, if step 8 or 7 clears in three minutes or less, the exposure is too short and should be increased on subsequent plates.

These rules apply, of course, only to plates on which the image areas have not become hardened too much by dark reaction. When a plate has been on the photo-composing machine too long, the image areas may take longer than three minutes to clear even though both the exposure and developer Baumé are correct. In such a case, you may be able to save the plate by using a developer one or two degrees lower in Baumé for the second and third applications. Complete clearing must take place on the regular image areas and on step 6 of the Sensitivity Guide image during the final development. Any gum residue left on the image areas will prevent the work from holding and the plate will be "blind". Don't depend on the deep-etching solution to remove any gum residue left on the image by incomplete development.

Chapter 11

DEEP-ETCHING THE PLATE

Deep-etching is the step that gives deep-etch plates their name. But, as was stated in Chapter 1, the etching of the image areas is not deep, but very shallow. The average etching depth is not over two to three ten-thousandths of an inch (.0002 to .0003 inch).

Our plate is now ready for the deep-etching step. The un-hardened coating has been removed from the image areas, but the non-image areas are covered with light-hardened coating called the "deep-etch stencil". This stencil must act as a "resist" to protect the non-image areas while the image areas are being etched.

Deep-etching mainly insures that the metal in the image areas will be less subject to frictional wear during printing. After cleaning to remove the black iron deposit formed during deep-etching, they are able to hold the printing image during long runs. But the etching also tends to give the image areas a sharp edge that improves their printing quality, particularly in halftones.

THE DEEP-ETCHING SOLUTION

The deep-etching solution contains a strong acid that attacks and eats away some of the plate metal in the image areas. And, since the stencil or resist on the non-image areas is affected by water, the deep-etching solution must, like the developer, contain a large amount of a salt like calcium chloride. Also the acid it contains must be suited to the plate metal.

113

Zinc, aluminum and stainless steel are quite different, so their deep-etching solutions must be properly formulated.

LTF recommends two deep-etching solutions, one for zinc and the other for aluminum and stainless steel plates. These are as follows:

Zinc Deep-Etching Solution

	Metric Units	U. S. Units
Calcium Chloride Solution, 40-41° Bé	1000 cc.	1 gallon
Iron Perchloride (FeCl$_3$), Lumps	25 g.	3¼ avoir. oz. (92 g.)
Hydrochloric Acid (HCl), C.P., 37.0-38.5%	19 cc.	2½ liq. oz. (71 cc.)

The Baumé of the finished solution should be 40-41 degrees at 77° F. Instructions for making the 40-41° Baumé calcium chloride solution are given in the Appendix.

Aluminum Deep-Etching Solution

	Metric Units	U. S. Units
Calcium Chloride Solution, 40-41° Bé	1000 cc.	89 liq. oz.
Zinc Chloride (ZnCl$_2$), Technical	380 g.	35½ avoir. oz.
Iron Perchloride (FeCl$_3$) Solution, 50-51° Bé	285 cc.	25¼ liq. oz.
Hydrochloric Acid (HCl), C.P., 37.0-38.5%	14 cc.	1¼ liq. oz. (37 cc.)
Cupric Chloride (CuCl$_2$ · 2H$_2$O)	27 g.	2½ avoir. oz. (70 g.)

The Baumé of the finished solution should be 50-51 degrees at 77° F. (25° C.). Instructions for preparing this solution, the 40-41° Bé. calcium chloride solution, and the 50-51° Bé. iron perchloride solution are given in the Appendix.

There are a number of good commercial deep-etching solutions. If you have used a commercial deep-etch coating and developer, it may be best to use the same brand of deep-etching solution.

The deep-etching solution for zinc plates doesn't work on aluminum plates. The aluminum deep-etching solution works well on stainless steel plates, but is too strong for zinc plates. Be sure you have the proper solution for your metal.

METHOD OF DEEP-ETCHING GRAINED ZINC PLATES

As soon as you have squeegeed the last developer off the plate, pour on a generous amount of zinc deep-etching solution. Work this evenly over the plate with the deep-etching pad in the same way as you did the developer. Continue rubbing

Figure 51. Deep-etching the plate.

for one-half to one and one-half minutes, then squeegee off the spent solution. Only one application is needed. The exact time of deep-etching will depend on two things: (1) the depth of etching you want, and (2) the temperature.

DEEP-ETCHING UNGRAINED ZINC PLATES

The deep-etching operation for ungrained zinc plates is just the same as for grained zinc plates. But there is a difference in the deep-etching solution and the time of its application.

For a suitable deep-etching solution, simply dissolve two and one-half ounces of cupric chloride ($CuCl_2.2H_2O$) in one gallon (or 20 grams in 1000 cc.) of zinc deep-etching solution. Do this regardless of whether you use the LTF formula (page 114) or a commercial solution.

Deep-etching will take about twice as long for ungrained as for grained plates because of the lack of grain and because there is a hard metal "skin" on the plate surface. The time of deep-etching will vary from one to three minutes, depending on the depth you want and the temperature.

METHOD OF DEEP-ETCHING GRAINED ALUMINUM PLATES

The actual operation of deep-etching is the same as for grained zinc plates. Only the deep-etching solution is different.

LTF recommends using a deep-etching solution that contains cupric chloride ($CuCl_2 \cdot 2H_2O$) like the formula on page 114. If you prefer to use a commercial aluminum deep-etching solution and it contains no copper salt, you can get the desired results by dissolving 2½ ounces of cupric chloride in one gallon (or 20 grams in 1000 cc.) of the solution.

Deep-etch the plate for one-half to one and one-half minutes, depending on the temperature and the depth you want. Then squeegee off the spent solution. In case the deep-etching solution should work too fast, try cutting down the amount of cupric chloride in the formula to 2 or even 1½ ounces.

DEEP-ETCHING UNGRAINED ALUMINUM PLATES

To deep-etch ungrained and brush-grained aluminum plates you use the same solution and technique as for grained aluminum plates. The time of etching, however, should be from one to three minutes, about twice as long, because of the resistance of the hard metal skin.

DEEP-ETCHING STAINLESS STEEL PLATES

In deep-etching stainless steel plates, you can use either the aluminum deep-etching solution (page 114) or straight 50-51° Baumé iron perchloride solution (see Appendix). The deep-etching time with the aluminum deep-etching solution will be somewhat longer than for aluminum plates. Straight 50-51° Baumé iron perchloride solution will etch somewhat faster than the aluminum deep-etching solution.

Discussion

Deep-etching is done in the same sink as the development without moving the plate. The deep-etching pad, like the developing pad, is a plush-covered wooden block. Keep the two pads separate and use each for its own purpose only. This will prevent contamination and possible damage to plates. As you get through using each pad, rinse it thoroughly with anhydrous alcohol, squeegee off the excess alcohol and stand it in a rack. This will prevent developer or deep-etching solution in the pads from taking up water from the air and ruining the next plate you work on. At the end of the day or shift, wash the pads with water, squeegee them as dry as possible and stand them in a rack to dry overnight.

*   *   *   *

LTF's recommended deep-etching solutions both contain iron perchloride. For aluminum plates and ungrained zinc plates, some cupric chloride ($CuCl_2$) is added to speed up and improve the uniformity of the etching. During deep-etching these salts are reduced and form a dark colored deposit on the image areas consisting of finely divided iron or a mixture of iron and copper. Most of this deposit, but not all, comes off during the following alcohol wash.

Formerly the deposit remaining after the alcohol wash was left on the image areas. However, occasional plate failures have indicated that it prevented good adhesion of the lacquer on zinc plates, and of the copper on copperized aluminum plates. For this reason some platemakers give their plates a treatment with deep-etch developer immediately after squeegeeing off the deep-etching solution and before the alcohol wash. This is called re-development. It removes part of the dark deposit, but not all.

LTF's research has definitely shown that the dark deposit on the image areas can cause early or spotty blinding of plates on the press. As a result, the Nicohol treatment was developed (Chapter 12). It removes the dark deposit completely.

*   *   *   *

Platemakers have different opinions as to how deep the image areas should be etched. In practice the average seems to be .0002 to .0003 inch. A greater depth than this is of no advantage in printing and requires too much time in re-graining plates to completely remove the old work. If the depth is more than about .0005 inch, halftones will not take ink properly from the rollers and will print hollow dots. Actually, good plates can be made with development alone, without any deep-etching. All that is really necessary is to remove all traces of the coating from the image areas so that the lacquer can bond tightly to the metal surface. However, LTF's experiments and shop practice show that a little deep-etching gives the plate better durability and printing quality.

As we said in Chapter 1, the platemaker doesn't need to measure the actual depth of etching. If he follows LTF instructions or the instructions provided by suppliers, the depth of etching will never be enough to cause trouble on the press. By working with the pressman and the plate grainer, he soon finds the etching depth that will satisfy both.

With any given deep-etching solution the only things that affect the etching depth are time of application and temperature. The longer the solution is allowed to act, the greater the image depth will be. And the higher the temperature, the faster the etch will work. If the shop is air conditioned, temperature variations are eliminated and all you have to control is the time. But, if not, and the shop temperature varies as it usually does, you can vary the time with temperature changes so as to get uniform depth from plate to plate. Different deep-etching solutions may have different rates of action and the time can be varied accordingly. For example, if your deep-etching solution gives a satisfactory depth in one minute at 75° F., you can change the time of application as the temperature changes according to the following table:

TEMPERATURE	DEEP-ETCHING TIME
60- 70° F.	1½ minutes
70- 80° F.	1 minute
80- 90° F.	45 seconds
90-100° F.	30 seconds

If the etching time at 75° F. is more or less than one minute, the times in the table can be changed proportionally.

*   *   *   *

Repeating what we said in Chapter 10, plates must be completely developed prior to being deep-etched. Gum residues on the image areas due to incomplete development prevent proper deep-etching. They are not removed by the deep-etching solution but remain on the metal. During printing the gum residue absorbs moisture so that lacquer and ink will no longer adhere to the image areas. The result is a blind plate.

Chapter 12

CLEANING THE IMAGE AREAS

The next logical step after deep-etching is to make the image areas properly ink receptive. On zinc plates, this involves applying non-blinding lacquer. On aluminum plates, it involves copperizing followed by the non-blinding lacquer application. But before these operations, we have to remove every last trace of deep-etching solution. Remember that both the developer and deep-etching solution contain large amounts of calcium chloride, or magnesium chloride, and zinc chloride. If even traces of these salts or of moisture remain on the deep-etched areas, lacquer will not stick to them. You can't wipe the solution off completely. You can't wash it off with water because water would remove most of the stencil that protects the non-image areas. You must use a solvent that will dissolve these salts but which will not affect the stencil. Anhydrous (water-free) ethyl alcohol is the solvent generally preferred.

To remove all of the dark deposit produced in deep-etching and obtain absolutely clean image areas, LTF developed the Nicohol solution. Comparative press tests have shown that plates treated with it have greater resistance to blinding than plates treated by any other known method.

Therefore, in view of past experience, two alternative methods of cleaning the image areas are given. One is the regular alcohol wash used for many years. The other is the new Nicohol treatment that laboratory and plant tests have shown to produce more consistently good plates. It does not apply to commercial deep-etching solutions with no iron perchloride.

119

If desired, redevelopment can be done immediately after deep-etching and before proceeding with the alcohol wash. Simply pour deep-etch developer on the plate and work it over the surface with a deep-etch developing pad, then squeegee it off and proceed with the alcohol wash.

Method No. 1: Anhydrous Alcohol Wash

With the plate still in the deep-etching sink, pour on a liberal amount of anhydrous (water-free) denatured alcohol. With a wad of paper wipes designed for this purpose, rub the entire plate surface evenly and thoroughly. Remove all the dark deposit you can from the image areas.

Figure 52. The plate must be washed four times with anhydrous alcohol to remove all traces of deep-etching solution.

Wipe off the alcohol and repeat the operation three times more, using fresh alcohol and clean paper wipes each time. After the fourth wash, rub the work areas thoroughly two or three times, using fresh paper wipes each time, to remove all the alcohol you can. Finally, fan the plate dry.

When you make the first application of alcohol, try to avoid spattering since it sometimes causes spots in halftones. A good method is to lay one or more paper wipes on the plate and pour the alcohol on them. Then use the same wipes to rub the alcohol over the plate. Another good method is to hold a paper wipe over the spout of the can when pouring the alcohol on the plate. You can control the flow by the pressure you apply on the wipe, and prevent spattering.

Cellosolve Solvent (ethyl cellosolve or ethylene glycol monoethyl ether) can be used instead of anhydrous alcohol. In this case it is best to make three applications of Cellosolve Solvent and a fourth application of anhydrous alcohol. Cellosolve Solvent evaporates quite slowly. If it doesn't dry completely before you apply the deep-etch lacquer, it could prevent the lacquer from holding. You can avoid this trouble by washing off the last of the Cellosolve with anhydrous alcohol.

Method No. 2: The Nicohol Treatment

With the plate still in the deep-etching sink, pour on a liberal amount of anhydrous alcohol. Rub it over the entire plate surface using a wad of paper wipes. Remove all the dark deposit you can from the image areas. Wipe off the excess alcohol and continue wiping with fresh paper wipes until the plate is dry.

Apply the Nicohol solution. Pour on a liberal amount and work it evenly over the entire plate with a deep-etching pad used only for this purpose. Continue working with the pad for about one minute or until all of the gray color has been removed and the image areas are clean and bright. Squeegee off and make another application of Nicohol solution for about 30 seconds. Wash off the Nicohol solution with two or three applications of anhydrous alcohol, using paper wipes. Finally, wipe the plate dry.

Whether the plate was given the alcohol wash only, or the Nicohol treatment, it is now ready for the stopping out of any unwanted areas according to the instructions in Chapter 13. Otherwise, if it is an aluminum plate, it is ready to be copperized (Chapter 14). If it is a zinc plate, it is ready for the application of non-blinding lacquer (Chapter 15).

Discussion

Suitable alcohols for use in deep-etch platemaking are Ansol M, Anhydrous Solox, Anhydrous Synacol, and Shellacol.

These are specially denatured ethyl alcohol (C_2H_5OH), approved for use in lacquers. Isopropyl alcohol (C_3H_7OH) is similar in solvent properties. The 99 per cent variety is entirely satisfactory. Apply it in exactly the same way as the anhydrous ethyl alcohols.

Use plenty of alcohol for each wash, especially in humid weather. While it is on the plate it is picking up moisture from the air. If you use too little, the moisture it picks up may dilute it enough to soften the gum stencil. Be sure to turn off the down-draft exhaust fan during the alcohol wash.

Also, in humid weather, be sure to wipe off all the alcohol you can before turning on the fan. If you have too much on, rapid evaporation may cool the plate so much that moisture will condense on it like it does on a glass of ice water. This could soften the stencil and cause a scummy plate. It could also cause blinding of the image areas.

Cellosolve Solvent costs more than the anhydrous alcohols but you need less of it. You can use smaller amounts because it doesn't pick up moisture from the air. To remove it, just sop it up and rub the plate dry with paper wipes. Giving a final wash with anhydrous alcohol is simply a safeguard.

Nicohol solution has the following formula:

Nicohol Solution

	Metric Units	U.S. Units
Cellosolve Solvent	900 cc.	3 quarts
Nitric Acid (HNO_3) Conc., Sp. Gr. 1.42	100 cc.	10 liq. oz.

When mixing the solution, be sure to pour the acid into the solvent slowly, with constant stirring. Otherwise the reaction may be violent and splash acid on you.

Cellosolve Solvent is ethylene glycol monoethyl ether. It is also sold under the names Dowanol EE, and Polysolve EE.*

Figure 53 shows photomicrographs of halftone dots on a deep-etched aluminum plate. Figure 53(a) shows an area in which the image was not treated with Nicohol. The dots show the dark iron deposit. Figure 53(b) shows an area on the same plate treated with Nicohol. The dark deposit is completely gone. The etching depth also appears greater.

---

*The cellosolves are manufactured by Carbide and Carbon Chemicals Corporation, Dow Chemical Company and Olin Mathieson Chemical Corporation.

 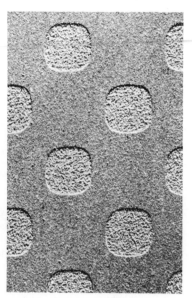

(a) Iron deposit in wells.   (b) Dots after Nicohol treatment.

Figure 53. Photomicrographs of etched dots, brush-grained aluminum, 60 second deep-etch, 12X.

It is possible for removal of the dark deposit to leave the image areas too deep. If the plate tends to print hollow halftone dots, the time of deep-etching should be shortened. This applies especially to zinc plates. The Nicohol solution itself doesn't do any etching on aluminum plates.

Chapter 13

STOPPING OUT UNWANTED AREAS

On photo-composed plates the regular work exposures don't usually cover the plate completely. There are almost always unexposed borders that would develop out and become printing areas unles something is done to protect them. This problem was mentioned briefly in Chapter 9, page 92. The three methods commonly used are as follows:

1. Masking the exposed work areas with aluminum foil or goldenrod paper and exposing the plate to an arc light to harden the unexposed borders.

2. Stopping or staging out the unexposed borders with shellac or lacquer before the development to protect them from the action of the developer and deep-etching solution.

3. Stopping or staging out the borders with deep-etch coating solution after the plate has been deep-etched to prevent them from taking the deep-etch lacquer and developing ink. In the case of aluminum plates, this prevents them from being copperized.

In addition to borders, there are almost always imperfections that must be stopped out to prevent them from printing. These are tape marks, film joint marks and dirt spots. It may also be necessary to stop out Sensitivity Guide images if they cannot appear on the printed sheets. These defects and the Sensitivity Guide images are usually stopped out by Method 3.

Which of the above methods is used to prevent the undesired areas from printing will depend on the nature of the form and the time and labor required. Often it is best to use one method for borders and another for tape marks, film joint marks, and dirt spots.

Masking the work areas and re-exposing the plate to eliminate borders is usually practiced when the form is regular and the masks required are simple rectangular shapes. But if irregular or intricate shapes would be required, it is better to stop out the borders with shellac, lacquer, or coating solution. Tape marks, joints and dirt spots are often hard to see before the plate is developed and are best stopped out with coating solution after deep-etching.

In this chapter we will discuss the stopping out with shellac or lacquer and deep-etch coating solution.

STOPPING-OUT MATERIALS

Stopping-out shellac can easily be made in the lithographic shop, if desired. Its formula is as follows:

Stopping-Out Shellac

	Metric Units	U. S. Units
Orange Shellac	250 g.	8 avoir. oz. (225 g.)
Anhydrous Denatured Alcohol (see Chapter 12)	1000 cc.	1 quart
Methyl Violet Dye	2 g.	1/16 avoir. oz. (2 g.)

LTF offers no formula for *stopping-out lacquer* since there are several excellent products available from suppliers. Preparation of a lacquer is too complicated to be practical in the lithographic shop.

Shellac and lacquer are for stopping out unwanted areas before development. For stopping out after deep-etching, use regular *deep-etch coating solution* (see Chapter 7).

METHOD OF STOPPING OUT BEFORE DEVELOPMENT

Paint out the unexposed borders and unwanted work areas with the stopping-out shellac or lacquer, using a soft brush, preferably camel's hair.

Discussion

Remember that the unhardened coating on the image areas of the plate is still light sensitive. Stopping out before development must therefore be done as quickly as possible under subdued, preferably orange, light. Unexposed borders are easy to see since they are a lighter color than the exposed areas.

Remember also, that, while you are working, the image areas are continuing to harden due to dark reaction. This hardening will be slow if the relative humidity is below 50 per cent and the temperature is 75° F. or lower, and you will usually have plenty of time. But, as the RH goes above 50 per cent and the temperature goes above 75° F., the time gets shorter rapidly. In figuring it, you have to include the time the plate was in the photo-composing machine. For example, if the RH gets up around 65 per cent, you only have a total of four to six hours for *exposure and stopping out* before the image areas get so hard they can't be developed properly. If photo-composing takes too much of this time, omit the stopping out before development and do it after the plate has been deep-etched. If the RH is 70 per cent or higher, do all necessary stopping-out only after deep-etching.

The stop-out shellac or lacquer remains on the plate while it is being developed and deep-etched. The alcohol wash (Chapter 12) then takes it off, leaving the deep-etch coating which was underneath it intact. This coating acts as part of the stencil and protects the unexposed borders while lacquer and developing ink are being applied.

As soon as the stop-out shellac or lacquer is dry, the plate is ready to be developed (see Chapter 10).

METHOD OF STOPPING OUT AFTER DEEP-ETCHING

Use either regular deep-etch coating solution, or deep-etch coating solution that has been acidified with phosphoric acid. To make the latter, simply add 3 to 4 cc. of 85 per cent phosphoric acid to 100 cc. (⅛ ounce to 3½ ounces) of coating solution.

Apply the coating solution to the unwanted areas with a camel's hair brush. Lay it on smoothly, about as thick as the original coating. When you have finished, dry the fresh coating under a fan for ten minutes.

If you use the regular deep-etch coating solution without acidifying it, LTF recommends that the stopped-out plate be set up in front of an arc lamp and given an overall light exposure to

Figure 54. Stopping-out unwanted areas with coating solution after the plate has been deep-etched.

harden the freshly applied coating. This exposure should be from one-half to three-fourths the time a deep-etch plate would need in a vacuum printing frame.

If you use the acidified deep-etch coating solution, the over-all light exposure isn't usually necessary.

Discussion

In stopping out after the plate has been deep-etched, you have two advantages: (1) You can work in bright light and clearly see minor defects that were hard to see before development, and (2) stopping-out time is not limited. Since there is no longer any coating on the image areas, there is no way that the plate can be damaged by excessive dark reaction.

The purpose of the additional light exposure after stopping out is to harden the coating painted on the unwanted areas. It does this in two ways: (1) by light-hardening the coating, and (2) by drying out any excess moisture. This light exposure also hardens the coating on any unexposed areas of the plate that may have been stopped out with shellac or lacquer before de-

Figure 55. The masked or stopped-out plate is given an overall exposure to the arc to harden unexposed borders or unwanted areas that have been stopped out with deep-etch coating solution.

velopment. The advantage of this is that the coating in the stopped-out areas is made more resistant to penetration by the deep-etch lacquer and developing ink.

The additional all-over light exposure is particularly important on *aluminum plates* if you intend to "copperize" the image areas before applying the deep-etch lacquer. The aluminum deep-etching solution (Chapter 11, page 114) produces some copper deposit on the image areas. But copperizing, which is discussed in Chapter 14, deposits a stronger copper layer and makes a more durable aluminum deep-etch plate. Stopped-out areas, where the coating hasn't been light hardened, are more easily penetrated by the copperizing solution than the rest of the gum stencil, and are likely to develop scum.

Chapter 14

COPPERIZING THE IMAGE AREAS ON ALUMINUM PLATES

Copperizing is usually done on aluminum plates. The object we are striving for in making a durable, high-quality lithographic plate is to produce image areas that have maximum ability to hold ink, and non-image areas that have maximum ability to hold a film of water. While aluminum can be well desensitized and given a high affinity for water, it is somewhat lacking in natural affinity for ink. The ink affinity of its image areas can, of course, be greatly improved by coating them with a suitable lacquer, but there is still some room for improvement in this direction.

Of all the metals we know, copper has the highest natural ink affinity. This is the reason that it has been chosen for the image areas of bimetal plates (see Introduction, page 5). This is also the reason that *copperizing* the image areas on aluminum deep-etch plates improves their durability and printing qualities. In spite of the fact that the chemical process of copperizing produces a much thinner layer of copper than electroplating, copperized aluminum plates are essentially bimetal plates.

It would seem that the copper image areas should eliminate the need for a deep-etch lacquer to hold the ink, but practical shop experience indicates that lacquer is still helpful. The lacquer seems to adhere to the copper image better than it does to aluminum.

The purpose in copperizing the image areas on aluminum plates is, therefore, to give them maximum affinity for the deep-etch lacquer. Then, if the lacquer should wear off, the image will still have a high affinity for ink.

Copperizing Solution for Aluminum Plates

	Metric Units	U. S. Units
Isopropyl Alcohol, 99%	1000 cc.	1 quart
Cuprous Chloride (Cu_2Cl_2)	31 g.	1 avoir. oz. (28.3 g.)
Hydrochloric Acid, 37.0-38.5%	32 cc.	1 liq. oz. (29.6 cc.)

Cuprous chloride is a different form of copper chloride than that used in LTF's deep-etching solution which was cupric chloride ($CuCl_2.2H_2O$). The two are not interchangeable. Instructions for making the copperizing solution are given in the Appendix.

There are also several good commercial copperizing solutions available from suppliers.

Figure 56. Copperizing the deep-etched areas of an aluminum plate.

METHOD OF COPPERIZING THE DEEP-ETCHED IMAGE

The aluminum plate has been deep-etched, and the deep-etching solution has been washed off with alcohol or Cellosolve Solvent, or treated with Nicohol solution to thoroughly clean the image areas. Unwanted areas and defects have been stopped out with deep-etch coating solution and their coating thoroughly dried or hardened by an overall light exposure. The plate has been returned to the deep-etching sink.

Pour some copperizing solution on the plate and spread it over the work areas with a plush-covered pad. Work it over the plate for three to five minutes, or until a reddish copper deposit is formed on the image areas. Then give the plate one or two washes with anhydrous alcohol to remove the copperizing solution. Wipe the plate dry with paper wipes and dry it thoroughly under a fan.

Discussion

If you have used the LTF Aluminum Deep-Etching Solution (Chapter 11, page 114), or a commercial deep-etching solution that contains cupric chloride, but have not given the plate the Nicohol treatment, you will find that copperizing of the image takes place quickly. Copper left by the deep-etching solution seems to make the reddish copper deposit form with greater ease and certainty than if the image was free from copper.

If you have given an aluminum plate the Nicohol treatment, the deep-etched image will be free from copper. In this case, the copperizing will take place a little slower and the copper deposit will be slightly different in color. However, tests have shown that this deposit adheres much better than when the Nicohol treatment is not used.

Good aluminum deep-etch plates can be made without copperizing. They are satisfactory for short and medium-length runs. The separate copperizing treatment, however, increases image durability and is definitely recommended for long runs. In either case, the Nicohol treatment after deep-etching insures better and more uniform bonding of lacquer, or copper plus lacquer, to the image areas, and improves the plate's resistance to blinding.

Chapter 15

APPLYING NON-BLINDING LACQUER

When the gum deep-etch process was in its infancy, several methods were used to make the image areas ink receptive after the alcohol wash. Some simply rubbed on a liquid developing ink. Others applied greasy ink with a hand roller. Still others applied a coating of asphaltum followed by a greasy ink. While good plates were made that ran long editions, too often they showed a tendency to become "blind" during printing, sometimes early in the run. The reason for this was obvious. Neither ink nor asphaltum could permanently protect the metal in the image areas against desensitization during printing. The press moisture, becoming emulsified in the ink, would carry gum and acid to the metal surface in the image areas. These would gradually become desensitized or "blind" and fail to take a full charge of ink from the form rollers. It was also too easy to blind a plate in gumming it up. The gum would penetrate the ink film and desensitize the metal underneath, producing blinding or gum streaks.

To correct this condition it was necessary to coat the deep-etched image areas with some moisture-impervious and ink-receptive material that wouldn't be dissolved by cleaning solvents or by the vehicle of the press ink, but would remain indefinitely as the image base.

The first material of this type that was tried was shellac. It was insoluble in petroleum solvents and turpentine and was very ink receptive. But it was not resistant enough to moisture

132

and would not prevent blinding during long press runs.

The next materials tried were nitrocellulose lacquers. These were used fairly successfully for a number of years. But they were not as ink receptive as could be desired and had a tendency to be desensitized by gum and acid in the press fountain water. Various other synthetic resins were tried but showed little or no improvement.

During recent years LTF's research brought to light the fact that certain synthetic vinyl resins had unusually high resistance to moisture and gum. Deep-etch lacquers made from them were extremely insoluble in cleaning solvents and ink vehicles but were very ink receptive. They also had excellent adhesion to the plate metals. Press tests showed that it was almost impossible to blind plates made with them or to produce gum streaks by gumming them up carelessly. Lacquers of this type were therefore called *non-blinding lacquers.*

Since these lacquers were developed by commercial lacquer houses for other purposes than deep-etch platemaking, their formulas could not be published. Information regarding them was therefore given to all interested suppliers of lithographic preparations. As a result, there are now available several excellent commercial non-blinding deep-etch lacquers.

*   *   *   *

The purpose, then, of applying a deep-etch lacquer to the image areas of the plate is to produce a permanent ink-receptive layer on them that is highly resistant to desensitization by gum and acids in the press fountain water.

METHOD OF APPLYING NON-BLINDING LACQUER

Pour a pool of non-blinding deep-etch lacquer on the plate and spread it over the image areas with a paper wipe. Then, with a soft lintless rag, rub it down to a smooth, even layer. Rub just hard enough to take most of the lacquer off the gum stencil that covers the non-image areas. Don't rub too hard since the idea is to leave as much lacquer on the image areas as you can.

In drying the lacquer, follow the supplier's instructions. The improved non-blinding lacquers generally work best if you dry them thoroughly before applying the developing ink.

Figure 57. Applying non-blinding lacquer to the deep-etched image areas.

Discussion

A good deep-etch lacquer should have the following qualities that make it easy to apply properly:

1. Its drying rate should be slow enough so you can rub it
down to an even film on your largest plates.

2. The dried lacquer film must be able to hold ink and resist
blinding during printing.

You can judge the first quality when you apply and rub the
lacquer down. If it dries too rapidly, it will get tacky and pull
lint out of the rag before you have it rubbed down. You won't
be able to rub it down smooth, and as a result, there will be
streaks of thick lacquer that will make the gum stencil very
hard or impossible to remove. On the other hand, too slow
drying will add unnecessarily to the platemaking time. It will
also tend to make you remove too much of the lacquer and to
leave too thin a film on the image areas, especially on solids.
In fact, these areas may wipe so clean that they can easily be
blinded. The non-blinding properties of the lacquer depend on
your leaving a reasonably thick lacquer film on the image.

The second "non-blinding" quality of the lacquer will show
up in that fewer plates have to be rubbed up or made over because of blindness or gum streaks. For a quick and sure way

to test this non-blinding quality, we refer you to LTF Bulletin No. 804, "How to Make and Run Deep-Etch Plates, Grained Zinc", page 51, and LTF Bulletin No. 806, "How to Make and Run Deep-Etch Plates, Aluminum", page 100.

Don't attempt to apply lacquer to a plate while it is in the deep-etching sink or on a table where there is a draft. A draft will dry and set the lacquer too quickly and you won't be able to rub it down to an even layer.

*   *   *   *

Great care should be taken to prevent lint from adhering to the lacquered image. Lint consists of cellulose fibers from paper wipes or rags. As soon as the plate starts to print, these fibers become saturated with water and in this condition they reject ink. As a result, the printed work will be full of white lines, just the size and shape of the fibers. Here are some don'ts that will help you avoid lint on the lacquered image:

1. Don't use a lacquer that dries and gets tacky (sticky) before you can rub it down smooth and uniform.

2. Don't use paper wipes to rub down the lacquer. You should use them only to spread the lacquer at first. Then use a lintless rag to rub it down. The surface of a deep-etch plate at this point is rough. Paper wipes aren't strong enough to stand the abrasion and break down. Some day paper wipes may be made that will not break down.

3. Don't use rags that are loosely woven or linty. Well washed cheesecloth or laundered new rags are best. Rags that have been laundered too much become weak and won't stand the abrasion. They should be avoided.

Deep-etch lacquer should be applied to aluminum plates whether or not the image areas have been copperized. While the copperized image areas theoretically should not need to be lacquered, the lacquer makes them take ink more readily on the press. It also makes them more resistant to blinding and gum streaks. While it is difficult to get absolute proof, there is evidence that lacquer sticks tighter to the copper image than to uncopperized aluminum.

Non-blinding deep-etch lacquer is essential in making ungrained zinc and aluminum deep-etch plates and stainless steel plates.

Chapter 16

APPLYING DEEP-ETCH DEVELOPING INK

The plate is now under (covered with) a film of deep-etch lacquer. But before we remove the hardened gum stencil from the non-image areas, it is necessary to apply a greasy deep-etch developing ink.

If a good non-blinding deep-etch lacquer was used, it might seem that the high ink receptivity and resistance to desensitization of the image areas would make developing ink unnecessary. This is partially true. Gum arabic and cellulose gum alone seem to have no effect on the bare lacquer. But a strong plate etch can injure its ink receptivity if the lacquer isn't protected by ink. There is no point in taking chances. Another important reason for applying developing ink is that the plate must be checked for errors and imperfections. The image must therefore be contrasty and visible in all its details. Even though the lacquer is colored, the color can't be made intense enough for easy inspection.

DEEP-ETCH DEVELOPING INK

The deep-etch developing ink is an intensely black liquid or plastic ink that is soft enough so you can rub it down to a thin, even film on the plate. It contains principally carbon black pigment, a non-drying greasy or waxy binder and a mixture of volatile solvents. It should dry entirely by evaporation, and remain soluble so it can be washed off later with a petroleum solvent or turpentine. It should not dry by oxidation like press ink, as this would make the film insoluble.

136

Liquid developing inks come in cans from which they can be poured. Plastic developing inks are sold in collapsible tubes from which they can be squeezed like tooth paste.

LTF doesn't offer a formula for deep-etch developing ink. The reason is that such an ink is hard to make properly, and the ingredients are too hard to specify accurately. A slight difference in the quality of an ingredient would make the difference between a good and a poor product. However, there are a number of good commercial deep-etch developing inks available from suppliers, and a platemaker can take his choice.

An important part of this step is that of powdering the dried developing ink. Its main purpose is to "set" the ink film and make it rub-proof so it can resist the scrubbing when you remove the gum stencil. The powder recommended by LTF is a 50-50 mixture of powdered talc (french chalk) and powdered rosin. Powdered talc alone can be used, but it tends to set the ink too hard and makes it difficult to remove with an ink solvent.

METHOD OF APPLYING DEVELOPING INK

Pour or squeeze some developing ink onto the plate and spread it over the image areas with a soft rag or paper wipe.

Figure 58. Applying developing ink to the lacquered plate.

Then, with a clean, soft rag rub the ink down to a smooth, even film and fan it dry. Finally powder the ink film with the talc-rosin mixture. You can do this by dipping a wad of dry cotton in the powder and simply rubbing it over the plate.

Figure 59. Powdering the inked plate with talc-rosin mixture.

If you are making ungrained zinc or aluminum deep-etch plates, the best type of developing ink to use is that supplied especially for bimetal plates. It is a special strong plastic ink that comes in tubes. When you apply it to the plate, rub it *into* the image areas, and continue rubbing until the ink builds up to a good, uniform film. This technique helps because the coating on ungrained plates is very thin, and the ordinary treatment tends to leave too little ink on the image areas.

Discussion

A good deep-etch developing ink is one that (1) is easy to smooth out to a thin, even film, (2) stays greasy enough after it has been powdered and the gum stencil removed so that gum won't stick to it, and (3) produces an intense black image that is easy to inspect for errors and imperfections. It is a good idea to try several different developing inks. Apply each ink to a different area on the same plate and then proceed to finish the plate. This will enable you to select the ink that works best and gives the best results.

In addition to setting the ink film, powdering reduces its greasiness somewhat. Too greasy an ink tends to repel the plate etch and gum so that areas close to solids, lines and dots are not fully desensitized. As a result, these areas tend to scum during printing, causing the work to thicken. Thus, powdering helps you get more uniform desensitization of the non-image areas.

It isn't always necessary to powder the developing ink. Some inks set harder than others and have less tendency to rub or smear after they have dried. If an ink dries hard enough to withstand scrubbing under warm water, and if your pressmen have no trouble with the image areas thickening during printing, you can omit the powdering step.

In applying the developing ink, be careful not to rub it down too thin. If the ink film is too thin, the etch and gum will not pull away and will tend to cover and dry over the work areas. This will make the plate hard to wash out and will necessitate a wet-wash on the press.

Chapter 17

REMOVING THE GUM STENCIL

The image areas of the plate have now been completely formed. They have been deep-etched, lacquered and coated with a greasy ink. All that remains to be done to finish the plate is to remove the protecting gum stencil from the non-image areas and to desensitize these areas to ink.

As we stated in Chapter 10, the light-hardened deep-etch coating that forms the stencil on the non-image areas doesn't resist water. This is the reason why a special developer was needed that contained calcium chloride or some other salt. It is also the reason why we had to use alcohol to wash off the deep-etching solution. Now that the image areas have been formed and protected, we can use water to take off the stencil.

METHOD OF REMOVING THE STENCIL

Place the plate in a tray or tank of warm water (90°-100° F.) and let it soak for about ten minutes. Then, while it is still under water, go over it with wad of cotton or a cellulose sponge to remove the ink and lacquer from the non-image areas. If you don't have a tray or tank, the initial ten-minute soaking and rubbing can be done in a trough under running water. But a tray is somewhat better.

The water must not be too hot. If it is above 100° F., the ink on the image areas may smear, even though it has been powdered.

Next, place the plate in a trough under running water, also at 90-100° F., and scrub off the stencil with a bristle brush.

140

Figure 60. Scrubbing off the deep-etch stencil. Use a bristle brush and running water.

Scrub until the non-image areas look clean and no longer feel slippery. While still under running water, polish out any dirt specks or unwanted marks with a snakeslip. Or you can drain off the water and use an abrasive air gun like the Paasche Air Eraser.

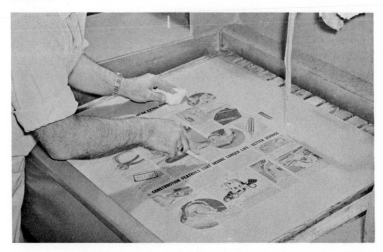

Figure 61. Dirt specks, unwanted register marks, and Sensitivity Guide images can be polished out with a snakeslip.

Discussion

There is a definite reason for soaking the plate before start-ing to scrub off the gum stencil. Soaking softens the stencil so it will come off with fairly light scrubbing. This minimizes the danger of smearing or removing ink from the image areas.

For removing the gum stencil, a brush made from vegetable fibers is best. Nylon and animal fibers have an affinity for ink even when they are wet with water. They tend to pick up some ink from the image and transfer it to non-image areas, causing scum streaks. Vegetable fibers are less likely to cause trouble because, once they are wet with water, they won't pick up the ink.

The temperature of the water is important. If it is too cold, its action in softening and removing the gum stencil will be slow and time-consuming. If it is too hot, it will tend to cause smearing of the ink. LTF has found that a water temperature of 90 to 100° F. is best for the stencil-removing operation. And the best way to control the water temperature is to install a constant-temperature mixing valve with cold and hot water connections. This valve can be adjusted to supply water at any temperature you want (see page 65).

If, for any reason, the developing ink smears when you scrub off the stencil, you can usually clean it up. Simply run cold water (60°-70° F.) over the plate and go over the image areas with a clean deep-etch developing pad. Never use wool flannel or felt to clean up the image areas. These materials pick up ink from the image and leave it insufficiently greasy.

*   *   *   *

If you are making aluminum or stainless steel plates, you are now ready to apply the desensitizing plate etch (Chapter 20). You can skip the steps described in Chapters 18 and 19. But, if you are making zinc deep-etch plates, don't omit these treat-ments. They are necessary to produce good desensitization.

Chapter 18

REMOVING RESIDUAL STENCIL FROM ZINC PLATES

After you have scrubbed off the deep-etch stencil, the non-image areas of the plate will look like clean, bare metal. Actually, the metal is not bare. It still is covered with a thin, invisible film of the light-hardened gum coating that can't be removed by scrubbing. This is called *residual stencil*. It is present regardless of the type of plate metal although zinc seems to hold more of it than aluminum or stainless steel.

The residual stencil is actually a water-receptive desensitizing layer. As long as it is present, ink can't attach itself permanently to the non-image areas of the plate and comes off as soon as the plate is dampened. For many years platemakers have considered the residual gum stencil an advantage and made no attempt to remove it. Its desensitizing action is so good that the only apparent reason for using a plate etch is to desensitize areas where dirt specks or unwanted work have had to be polished out with a snakeslip or other abrasive.

The only ways the residual stencil can be removed are by abrasion or chemical action. But whether there is any advantage gained depends on whether its removal helps to improve the final desensitization. LTF's research has shown that, with aluminum and stainless steel plates, removing the residual stencil doesn't improve the desensitization and is of no advantage. So, if you are using aluminum or stainless steel, you can skip the operations described in Chapters 18 and 19 and go directly to Chapter 20 on desensitization.

143

In the case of grained zinc plates, removing the residual stencil is of no advantage if you use a gum-bichromate plate etch (see Appendix). So, if you are working with zinc plates and plan to use a gum-bichromate etch, you can skip the steps described in Chapters 18 and 19 and go directly to Chapter 20 on desensitization. But the desensitization produced by this method is not the best.

If you are using zinc plates and want to give them the best possible desensitization, you will plan to use a cellulose gum plate etch, or a tannic-alum plate etch (see Appendix). In this case you must remove the residual stencil as described in the present chapter. You must also give the plate a post-treatment as described in Chapter 19. (Post-treatments are chemical surface treatments of the bared non-image areas of the plate. They are similar to the *pre-treatments* described in Chapter 6.)

Because of their smoothness, ungrained zinc deep-etch plates require the best possible desensitization. On them the residual stencil should always be removed. Then they should be given a post-treatment and desensitized with a cellulose gum plate etch.

METHOD OF REMOVING RESIDUAL STENCIL
(FOR ZINC PLATES ONLY)

Remove the residual stencil immediately after you have scrubbed off the stencil (Chapter 17). To do this, you use diluted deep-etch developer made as follows:

Deep-Etch Developer	1 part
Water	3 parts

You can use either the regular deep-etch developer or the stabilized deep-etch developer (Chapter 10, page 105), or any good commercial deep-etch developer.

Pour the diluted developer on the plate and work it over the entire surface with a wad of cotton for about one minute. Then flush it off thoroughly with water and squeegee off the excess water.

The plate is now ready to be post-treated.

Discussion

Not much is known about the chemistry of plate desensitization. However, we do know that desensitization is the result of forming a thin hydrophilic (water-loving) film of a colloid on the metal surface, that acts as an ink barrier. It keeps ink from actually contacting the metal surface where it would stick. Ink will stick to the colloid film when it is dry, but when it is dampened the film absorbs water and releases the ink. This is a basic principle. Without the desensitizing film, lithographic printing as we know it wouldn't be practical.

Theoretical reasoning hasn't been of much help in research on desensitization. What knowledge we have has been gotten largely by cut-and-try experiments. But research has shown us that the proper preparation of zinc plates to receive the desensitizing etch is a very important factor in producing good desensitization. As a result of many tests we now know that:

1. On aluminum and stainless steel plates, the desensitization is not improved by removing residual stencil or by post-treating the non-image areas.

2. On zinc plates, removing the residual stencil and post-treating the non-image areas, followed by desensitization with a cellulose gum plate etch, gives the best desensitization. This procedure is a must for ungrained zinc plates.

3. On grained zinc plates, good desensitization can be obtained if the residual stencil is not removed. In this case, almost any good plate etch will make plates that are satisfactory for short and medium-length runs, but which won't stand up for as long runs as plates treated as in No. 2 (above).

Chapter 19

SURFACE POST-TREATMENTS FOR ZINC PLATES

Surface post-treatments are chemical surface treatments of the bared, non-image areas of zinc plates. They are applied after removing the residual stencil (Chapter 18) and before desensitization (Chapter 20). They are called post-treatments to distinguish them from similar treatments of the plate surface prior to coating it with the light-sensitive deep-etch coating solution. The latter are called pre-treatments and were described in Chapter 6.

The chemical reactions on the zinc surface when it is post-treated are not known. All we do know is that the surface is changed in such a way that the desensitization obtained with plate etches is greatly improved. As we said before, removal of the residual stencil, followed by a post-treatment and desensitization with a cellulose gum etch, gives zinc plates the best desensitization we know how to produce on them. Post-treatments also tend to prevent streaking when the plate etch is applied.

So far, no post-treatments have been found that improve the desensitization of aluminum and stainless steel plates. Even without post-treatments the desensitization of these metals is better than the best we can obtain on zinc plates even with post-treatments.

Three solutions have been developed for post-treating zinc plates. These are the Cronak, Phosphate, and Nital solutions. Extensive testing has shown them to be almost equally good.

If anything, the newest of the three, the Nital solution, is slightly the best. Formulas for all three and instructions for their use will be given.

Before applying any post-treatment, be sure that all clean-up erasures have been made and any unwanted work removed.

POST-CRONAK

The solution used for the Post-Cronak treatment is exactly the same as that for the Pre-Cronak treatment described in Chapter 6, page 51. Its formula is as follows:

The Cronak Solution

	Metric Units	U. S. Units
Ammonium Bichromate,		
[$(NH_4)_2Cr_2O_7$], Photo Grade	360 g.	12 avoir. oz. (340 g.)
Water	20 liters	5 gallons
Sulfuric Acid (H_2SO_4), Sp. Gr. 1.84	63 cc.	2 liq. oz. (59 cc.)

The finished solution should have a pH value between 1.4 and 1.7. Instructions for preparing and testing it are given in the Appendix. For precautions in making and handling the Cronak solution, review Chapter 3, page 23.

Post-Cronaking Zinc Plates

After having removed the residual stencil and squeegeed off the excess water, put some Cronak solution in each of two wide-mouth bottles and proceed as follows:

1. Holding the two bottles, one in each hand, dump the solution quickly onto the plate, first from one side and then from the other. The idea is to cover the plate with solution as quickly as possible. Let the solution stand on the plate for thirty seconds to one minute.

2. Flush the Cronak solution off the plate until the wash water shows no more yellow color.

3. With water running on the plate, go over the surface with a wad of cotton, rubbing lightly. Flush the plate with water again, and squeegee off the excess.

The plate is now ready to be desensitized.

Discussion

The Post-Cronak treatment does a very good job of preparing zinc plates to receive the desensitizing etch. Both laboratory and commercial runs have shown that, when followed with a cellulose gum plate etch, Post-Cronak gives plates that run clean and stand up for long editions. However, Post-Cronak has one serious disadvantage; the bichromate in the Cronak solution can cause dermatitis (see Chapter 3, page 24). In handling it, rubber gloves should be used and great care taken to keep it off the skin.

The Post-Cronak treatment tends to leave a brown stain on the non-image areas of the plate. This stain doesn't seem to affect the printing quality.

Because of the dermatitis hazard, LTF favors the Post-Phosphate and Post-Nital treatments.

POST-PHOSPHATE

The Post-Phosphate treatment is a modification of a plate-etching treatment originally developed by the Swedish Graphic Arts Laboratory. LTF's experiments showed that, on deep-etch zinc plates, it does an excellent job of preparing the metal to receive the desensitizing etch. In fact, with a cellulose gum plate etch, it does as good or even a better job than Post-Cronak. And, since it eliminates the use of bichromate, it also does away with the dermatitis hazard.

The Phosphate Solution, Formula No. 1

	Metric Units	U. S. Units
Aluminum Sulfate		
$[Al_2(SO_4)_3 \cdot 18H_2O]$	15 g.	2 avoir. oz. (57 g.)
Potassium Nitrate (KNO_3)	11.5 g.	1½ avoir. oz. (42.5 g.)
Ammonium Phosphate, Monobasic		
($NH_4H_2PO_4$)	20.5 g.	2¾ avoir. oz. (78 g.)
Water	1000 cc.	1 gallon

The finished Phosphate solution should have a pH value between 2.4 and 2.6. Instructions for preparing and testing it are given in the Appendix.

Post-Phosphating Zinc Plates

Apply the Phosphate solution like a counter-etch. Pour a liberal amount on the plate and then rock it back and forth for one minute to insure complete and uniform coverage. Then flush the plate with water, rubbing the surface lightly but thoroughly with a wad of cotton. Squeegee off the excess water.

The plate is now ready to be desensitized.

Discussion

The Post-Phosphate treatment does an excellent job of preparing the non-image areas of the plate to receive the etch. As we said before, it gives as good or better desensitization than Post-Cronak. Its one disadvantage is that plates made with it can't be desensitized with an etch containing a bichromate. There is some reaction between the bichromate and the phosphated zinc surface that prevents good desensitization and causes scumming.

POST-NITAL

The Post-Nital treatment was a somewhat accidental discovery. In running tests with different counter-etches, one of those included was to be the well-known nitric acid-alum mixture. But instead of the *potassium* alum normally used, the operator made up the solution with *ammonium* alum. Results of the test showed that this counter-etch was not good for the image areas of the plate, but it resulted in excellent desensitization of the non-image areas. Additional tests in which we varied the amount of nitric acid in the solution resulted in still further improvement of desensitization.

The Post-Nital treatment has all of the advantages of Post-Cronak and Post-Phosphate, but none of their disadvantages. It can't cause dermatitis because it contains no bichromate. And, unlike Post-Phosphate, you can follow it with any type of plate etch.

The Nital Solution

	Metric Units	U. S. Units
Ammonium Alum,		
$[NH_4Al\,(SO_4)_2 \cdot 12H_2O]$	30 g.	4 avoir. oz. (113 g.)
Nitric Acid (HNO_3), Sp. Gr. 1.42	1 cc.	⅛ liq. oz. (3.7 cc.)
Water	1000 cc.	1 gallon

The Nital solution should have a pH value between 2.4 and 2.6. Instructions for making and testing this solution are given in the Appendix.

The Post-Nital Treatment

As in the Post-Phosphate treatment, you apply the Nital solution just like you would a counter-etch. Pour a liberal amount on the plate and then rock it back and forth for 30 seconds to one minute to insure complete and uniform coverage. Then you flush it off with water, while going over the plate with a wad of cotton. When you have squeegeed off the excess water, the plate is ready to be etched.

Discussion

The Post-Nital treatment does at least as good a job as Post-Cronak or Post-Phosphate in preparing the non-image areas of the plate to receive the desensitizing etch. Some think it even better. And it is free from their disadvantages. The Nital solution contains only two chemicals, is very easy to prepare, and forms no precipitate or sediment. It contains no chemical that could cause dermatitis, and works with both bichromate and non-bichromate plate etches. Shops that have tried the Post-Nital treatment have reported excellent results.

Chapter 20

DESENSITIZING THE PLATE

Etching is the lithographic shop expression for the step of desensitizing the non-image areas of the plate. In other trades, like photoengraving, it means "biting or eating into."

In lithography, the term "etching" has come down to us from the days of printing from stones. Desensitization was then done with gum arabic and nitric acid, and the non-image areas were often etched to some depth, leaving the image areas in slight relief. With metal plates the action on the non-image areas is different. The purpose of the plate etch is not to remove metal, but to add a thin, invisible, but tightly adhering, water-receptive gum film to the non-image areas. This film acts as a barrier to prevent ink from contacting and sticking to the plate metal. In other words, it desensitizes the metal to ink.

Etching or desensitizing the plate is an absolutely necessary step. If it couldn't be done, lithography would never have become a practical commercial printing process. Theoretically, you could print with only a water film on the non-image areas. But accidental drying of the plate would allow ink to contact the metal, and once this happened, the plate would be ruined. With a desensitizing gum film on the non-image areas, a water film is still necessary for printing, but accidental drying and inking up of the non-image areas does no harm. When the plate is again dampened, the ink is released and the plate "cleans up."

151

PLATE ETCHES

Plate etches are solutions of gum arabic or cellulose gum to which certain acids and salts have been added. There are a number of good commercial plate etches available for zinc and aluminum. But, if you prefer to make your own, LTF recommends the following formulas.

Cellulose Gum Plate Etch for Zinc

	Metric Units	U. S. Units
Water	750 cc.	3 quarts
Phosphoric Acid (H_3PO_4), 85%	7.8 cc.	1 liq. oz. (29.5 cc.)
Magnesium Nitrate, Crystals, [$Mg(NO_3)_2 \cdot 6H_2O$]	11.3 g.	1½ avoir. oz. (42.5 g.)
Cellulose Gum, Dry	41 g.	5½ avoir. oz. (156 g.)
Water to make	1000 cc.	1 gallon

This plate etch should have a pH value between 2.9 and 3.3. For instructions on making and testing it (see the Appendix). Sources of cellulose gum are also given.

Gum Arabic Plate Etch for Zinc, Formula No. 1

	Metric Units	U.S. Units
Water	340 cc.	40 liq. oz.
Tannic Acid	20.0 g.	2¾ avoir. oz. (78 g.)
Chrome Alum [$KCr(SO_4)_2 \cdot 12H_2O$]	30.6 g.	4 avoir. oz. (113 g.)
Phosphoric Acid (H_3PO_4), 85%	10.9 cc.	2¾ liq. oz. (81 cc.)
Gum Arabic Solution, 14° Bé	680 cc.	88 liq. oz.

The final pH value of this plate etch should be 1.8 to 2.0.

Gum Arabic Plate Etch for Zinc, Formula No. 2

	Metric Units	U. S. Units
Water	30 cc.	4 liq. oz. (118 cc.)
Ammonium Bichromate [$(NH_4)_2Cr_2O_7$], C.P. or Photo Grade	7.5 g.	1 avoir. oz. (28.3 g.)
Gum Arabic Solution, 12-14° Bé	945 cc.	121 liq. oz.
Phosphoric Acid (H_3PO_4), 85%	18.5 cc.	2⅜ liq. oz. (70 cc.)

The finished plate etch should test between 2.0 and 2.5 pH. Instructions for preparing and testing these two gum arabic plate etches are given in the Appendix. Instructions for making 14° Baumé gum arabic solution are also given in the Appendix.

Gum Arabic Plate Etch for Aluminum and Stainless Steel

	Metric Units	U. S. Units
Gum Arabic Solution, 12-14° Bé	1000 cc.	1 gallon
Phosphoric Acid (H_3PO_4), 85%	31 cc.	4 liq. oz. (118 cc.)

Simply add the phosphoric acid to the gum solution and mix
thoroughly. This etch should have a pH value of 1.9 to 2.1.

METHOD OF DESENSITIZING THE PLATE

Squeegee any excess water off the cleared or post-treated
plate and transfer the plate to the gumming table. A good idea
is to lay it on a pad of newsprint sheets somewhat larger than
the plate. The paper keeps the etch and gum solution off the
table top. It can be renewed and makes for clean operation.

Figure 62. Desensitizing the plate with plate etch.

Pour a liberal amount of etch on the plate and work it
over the entire surface in both directions for one to two minutes with a soft brush or sponge. Then, with a soft, clean
cloth, rub the etch down smooth and fan it thoroughly dry.

For small plates, only one application of plate etch is necessary. But for plates larger than 35"x45", it is a good idea to
apply the etch a second time, rub it down and fan dry. A large

plate is hard to cover uniformly, and etching a second time insures that all areas will be treated the same.

Discussion

The results of many tests have shown that the method of applying the etch is just as important as having the proper chemicals in the etch. For many years platemakers simply worked the etch over the plate surface for one to two minutes, then flushed it off and gummed up the plate. While this produced some degree of desensitization, it was not very durable and plates too easily became sensitive to ink during printing. Experiments have shown, however, that very much better desensitization is obtained when the etch is dried down thoroughly before it is washed off. Then the desensitizing gum film sticks much tighter and the plate will have a much longer scum-free printing life.

Drying the etch down on the plate is important on all types of metal plates, whether grained or ungrained, regardless of which etch formula or commercial plate etch you use.

*   *   *   *

The only materials we know of that produce good desensitizing films are water-soluble gums that contain acid groups, namely, carboxyl (COOH) and hydroxyl (OH), in their molecules. The known gums of this type most practical to use are gum arabic and cellulose gum (see Chapter 3, pages 25 and 37). We think that their carboxyl and hydroxyl groups cause them to be "adsorbed" (held as thin, insoluble films) on metal surfaces. But these groups must be free to be adsorbed. In gum arabic they are combined with calcium, magnesium and potassium. In cellulose gum they are combined with sodium. This is why phosphoric acid and acid salts are used in plate etches. They take the calcium, magnesium, potassium and sodium away from the gum and leave its acid groups free.

Plain gum arabic and cellulose gum solutions, if they are spread on a clean metal surface and then washed off with water, leave a desensitizing film. But this film is weak and loosely held, and is not durable enough for printing. If these solutions are dried down on the metal surface before they are washed off, the desensitizing film is stronger and sticks tighter. But it still is too weak for practical printing. Really good desensitization is only obtained when the gum is made acid to free its carboxyl and hydroxyl groups. And the amount of acid used to do this is important. Gum arabic etches are most effective when their pH values are below 2.5. Cellulose gum etches produce the best results when their pH values are about 3.0.

As we said in Chapter 18, we know very little about the chemistry of desensitization. All that we know is how to produce it, and this we have found out by cut-and-try experimentation. The same is true with regard to the formulation of plate etches. Many gum, acid, and salt combinations have been tried. We have found some better than others, but we can't say that we have found the best possible combinations. There are still possibilities for improvement.

For more discussion of desensitizing gums, see LTF Bulletin No. 401, "Chemistry of Lithography".

*   *   *   *

Comparative press tests made by LTF have shown that the cellulose gum plate etch, applied after a post-treatment, gives zinc plates the best desensitization. The gum arabic plate etch, Formula No. 1, gives very good desensitization and, when used, the plate doesn't have to be post-treated. The gum arabic plate etch, Formula No. 2, while good, hasn't shown up as well as Formula No. 1 in our tests. Also, since Formula No. 2 contains a bichromate, there is the hazard of dermatitis. Formula No. 2 is included here mainly because it has been published in a number of other LTF bulletins. It is not recommended.

Many plate etches for aluminum have been tested, but the one shown in this Chapter has always shown up the best so far. Aluminum and stainless steel plates desensitize best without removal of the residual stencil and without a post-treatment. In fact, these metals are naturally more water receptive than zinc and can be desensitized more completely. The ability of aluminum to run clean on the press has caused many shops to prefer it.

*   *   *   *

In etching plates it is important to use fresh, uncontaminated etching solution each time you apply it. It is best not to have the plate dry. The amount of water left on the plate by the squeegee is about right. Any excess water would dilute and weaken the etch.

Be careful not to contaminate fresh etch with etch that has been on the plate. After you have used a brush or sponge to spread the etch, squeeze out all the etch you can from it into

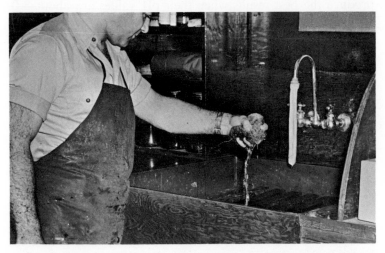

Figure 63. Squeeze the used and weakened etch out of the sponge into the sink so it won't contaminate the fresh etch.

the sink so it won't contaminate fresh etch when you make a second application or etch another plate. Etch that has been on the plate will have lost its strength, and if mixed with fresh etch will weaken it.

Don't use a new natural sponge to apply or spread the plate etch. New sponges are strongly alkaline and will weaken the etch by neutralizing the acid in it. You should always break in a natural sponge by washing it several times in a counter-etch (see Chapter 5, page 45) to neutralize its alkalinity, and then rinsing it thoroughly in tap water.

Chapter 21

GUMMING UP THE PLATE

As soon as a plate has been desensitized, it is capable of printing. Theoretically it could, at this point, be put on a press and a run started. But there are practical reasons why this is not done. Before it goes to press, the plate must be carefully inspected to be sure there have been no errors in the work. There may be work areas to be removed or corrected. Sometimes additions have to be made. And, since presses must be kept busy, press runs are scheduled and plates must be ready on time. For these reasons plates are usually made well ahead of time so presses won't be held up waiting for them.

During the interval between its desensitization and starting the press run, the plate must be protected from mechanical damage. Without protection, its non-image areas could easily be rubbed or scratched, and this would damage their thin desensitizing film. And if such damage occurred in halftone areas, it couldn't be repaired. To provide the necessary protection from mechanical damage, the non-image areas must be given a coating of gum. This operation is called *gumming up the plate*.

Another reason for gumming up is that most plates have to be washed out and put under asphaltum. By this we mean that the developing ink must be washed off the image areas and replaced with a thin film of asphaltum. To carry out these operations properly, the non-image areas of the plate must be protected by a gum film.

GUMMING-UP MATERIALS

The gum most generally used to protect the plate is gum arabic. It is applied in the form of an 8° to 10° Baumé solution which is spread over the entire plate, rubbed down to a thin, even film, and then fanned dry. Other gums that have been used include mesquite gum, dextrine, and cellulose gum. You can either make your own gum solution or buy it from a supplier. Commercial gum solutions may or may not contain gum arabic and this will usually be stated on their labels.

The formula and method of preparing 14° Baumé gum arabic solution are given in the Appendix. To make the 8° or 10° Baumé solution, simply add water. The only other materials needed are a clean sponge and clean, soft rags.

METHOD OF GUMMING UP THE PLATE

At this point the plate is covered with a thin coating of dried plate etch which must be washed off. To do this you don't need to put the plate back in the sink. Leave it on the etching table and simply wash it off with a water-soaked sponge. Go over the plate with the water sponge, then squeeze out and re-wet the sponge with fresh water. Go over the plate two or three times more with fresh water, then squeeze out the sponge and use it to remove as much water as you can, leaving the plate just damp.

Pour some gum solution on the plate and use the sponge to spread it over the entire surface. Squeeze out the sponge and go over the plate again to remove excess gum solution. Now, take a slightly damp clean rag and rub the gum down smooth. Finally take a clean, dry rag and rub the entire surface vigorously until the gum coating looks and feels dry. Turn on the fan to dry the coating thoroughly.

Discussion

The main purpose in gumming up a plate is to leave as much gum as possible on the non-image areas without covering the image areas. The greasy developing ink that covers the image areas helps you do this by repelling the gum solution. But to do a good job requires experience.

Figure 64. Steps in gumming up the plate.

(a) Wash the plate three times with clean water, using a sponge. Wring out the sponge and use it to take off excess water.

(b) Apply a liberal amount of gum solution.

(c) Work the gum over the plate for about one minute. Squeeze out the sponge and use it to take off the excess gum.

(d) Use a slightly damp rag to rub the gum down smooth. Finally use a clean dry rag to rub the gum dry.

(e) Fan the plate to dry the gum film thoroughly.

If the gum is rubbed down too thin on the non-image areas, it may not give them enough protection from mechanical damage. And later on, after asphaltum has been applied, there may not be enough gum to release the asphaltum from the non-image areas when the plate is washed with water. If this happens, the plate may be very hard to clean up and get into printing condition.

On the other hand, if too much gum is left on the plate, it is likely to cover some of the image areas. If it does, you will find it very difficult or even impossible to wash out the developing ink with a solvent so that asphaltum can be applied. This, too, will make extra work necessary to get the plate in printing condition.

To see if you have done a good gumming job, look across the plate at a low angle toward a bright light. If the image areas are all free from gum, they will appear dull. But, if you see shiny spots or streaks anywhere in the image areas, these are caused by dried gum covering up the work. Remove this gum immediately by going over the plate with a soft rag that has been dampened and wrung out as dry as possible. Check the plate again to be sure no shiny spots remain. If there are, the best thing to do is to wash off all the gum with a water sponge and start over, using a thinner gum solution or rubbing down the gum somewhat harder toward the end.

*   *   *   *

If you find it hard to apply the gum without covering the image areas, the trouble may be due to a developing ink that isn't greasy enough to repel your gum solution. Or it may be due to your having rubbed the developing ink down too thin. Still another cause would be scrubbing the plate with wool flannel in the process of removing the deep-etch stencil (Chapter 17, page 142). If you can't gum up the plate without leaving gum on the image areas, wash off the gum with water. Then rub up or roll up the plate with ink to make the image greasier. After this treatment you should have no further trouble.

To rub up a plate, use a special non-drying ink called "rolling-up black". Place some of this ink on a slab and work it well with an ink knife. If it is too stiff, soften it by adding a little 00 linseed varnish until it just begins to flow.

Moisten a rag slightly with Lithotine (Chapter 3, page 34) or turpentine. Dampen the plate with a water sponge and go over the image areas with the solvent to soften the developing ink. Then pat the rag in the rolling-up ink and, while keeping the plate damp, go over the image areas with the inked rag until they take on a good black color. Wash the plate with the water sponge to remove any ink remaining on the non-image areas, fan it dry, and then powder the image with the talc-rosin mixture (Chapter 16, page 138). After this has been done, you should have no trouble gumming up the plate.

If, when rubbed up, the image has thickened, or if ink tends to stick to the non-image areas, you can usually correct this condition by rolling up the plate. Use a leather hand roller, and roll some of the ink out to a uniform film on the slab. Dampen the plate and roll up the image until the plate starts to dry. Charge the roller with ink again, re-dampen the plate, and roll up the image again. Repeat until the image pulls out clean and sharp. Dry the plate, powder the image, and proceed to gum it up.

Both rubbing up and rolling up a plate require considerable skill. The trick is to get the image areas to take ink without having any ink stick to the non-image areas. If possible have someone with experience show you how to perform these operations before you try them.

*   *   *   *

General shop experience seems to indicate that gum arabic is the best material for gumming up plates. Some shops use mesquite gum and claim that it has less tendency to cover up the image areas.

Cellulose gum can be used but requires special precautions. While 14° Baumé gum arabic solution contains 25 per cent gum, an equally viscous cellulose gum solution contains only 6 per cent. This means that, when you gum up a plate with cellulose gum solution, you leave only about one-fourth as much gum on the non-image areas if you apply it the same as gum arabic solution. In gumming up plates with cellulose gum, you have to leave more gum on the plate. You do this by rub-

Figure 65. Steps in rolling up a plate.

(a) Wash the gum off the plate thoroughly with a sponge and clean water.

(b) While the plate is still damp, apply Lithotine and remove the developing ink with a clean rag.

(c) Pat a soft, slightly damp rag in rolling-up ink that has been thinned slightly with 00 varnish.

(d) Dampen the plate with the sponge and rub the inked rag lightly over the image areas. Don't let the plate dry. Keep it damp by squeezing a little water on it from the sponge.

(e) When the entire image has taken ink, wash the plate with the water sponge and take off excess water. Roll up the plate with a hand roller and roll-up ink. Keep on rolling until the plate starts to dry.

(f) Recharge the hand roller with ink, re-dampen the plate, and roll it up again. Repeat this until the image is fully inked and sharp, and the background is clean.

bing down the solution more lightly. This is a technique that has to be learned. If you rub cellulose gum down too thin, the non-image areas won't clean up after the image areas have been put under asphaltum (see page 160).

Dextrine was used for gumming up plates during World War II by European lithographers when their supply of gum arabic was cut off. It tided them over the emergency but was not considered a satisfactory gumming-up medium.

Chapter 22

PUTTING THE PLATE UNDER ASPHALTUM

The final step in preparing a deep-etch plate for printing is to remove the developing ink from the image areas and replace it with a thin layer of asphaltum. Sometimes this is done by the platemaker and sometimes by the pressman. Practice varies with circumstances.

The image on the etched and gummed plate is under black developing ink. And since the pressman should always check the plate for errors and general quality before starting the press run, it is the practice in many shops for the platemaker to leave the plate under developing ink. Then, after it has been checked, the pressman washes out the developing ink and puts the image under asphaltum.

Unfortunately, some developing inks tend to dry so that after the plate has stood for a few days the ink can't be washed out with Lithotine or turpentine. And, if it isn't washed out completely, the image may refuse to take ink on the press. So, if the plate is not to go to press for 24 hours or longer, it is best for the platemaker to put it under asphaltum.

THE ASPHALTUM SOLUTION

There are a number of good commercial "washout" solutions available from suppliers. These are based on asphaltum but most of them contain other ingredients such as greases and fatty acids that are believed to be beneficial. Asphaltum alone makes a good washout solution, and if you prefer to make your own, the following formula is recommended:

Asphaltum Solution

	Metric Units	U. S. Units
Powdered Asphaltum or Gilsonite,		
Turpentine Soluble	175 g.	23 avoir. oz. (650 g.)
Lithotine or Turpentine	1000 cc.	1 gallon

Instructions for making asphaltum solution and Lithotine are given in the Appendix.

METHOD OF APPLYING ASPHALTUM

Before washing out the developing ink and putting the image under asphaltum, make sure that (1) the gum on the non-image areas of the plate is thoroughly dry, and (2) there is no gum covering any part of the image area (see Chapter 21, page 160). If the gum on the non-image area is not thoroughly dry, it may be penetrated by the ink solvent or by the asphaltum solution. This would make the plate hard to clean up and might cause scumming.

If any of the image areas are covered with dried gum, you won't be able to do a good job of washing out the developing ink. Look at the reflection of light from the plate surface at a low angle. Any gum on the work areas will appear shiny. If free from gum, these areas will appear dull. If there is any gum on the work areas, follow the instructions in Chapter 21, page 160, to remove it.

Wash off the developing ink with Lithotine or turpentine, using a clean, soft rag. The ink should come off easily with very little rubbing. Pour on some asphaltum solution (or commercial "washout solution") and spread it over the work areas. You can use the same rag for this purpose. Then use a dry rag to rub down the asphaltum to a thin, even layer, and fan dry.

Discussion

If a deep-etch plate has been made with a good non-blinding lacquer (Chapter 15) it would seem theoretically unnecessary to coat the image areas with asphaltum at this point. But practically, asphaltum seems to be beneficial. It protects the lacquer surface from contamination and makes it take ink more readily on the press.

Correctly applied, the asphaltum film will be a light tan color and will be transparent. Such a film is easily removed by the pressman when he washes the gum off the non-image areas with his water sponge. If the asphaltum is put on too thick, it will be hard to wash off the non-image areas. Scummy plates are often blamed on asphaltum penetrating the gum layer, when the actual cause is that it was put on too thick.

*   *   *   *

A few shops have reported that washing out the image on copperized aluminum plates (Chapter 14) and on copper-image bimetal plates with turpentine has caused blinding of the image areas (refusal of the image areas to take ink on the press). At least one shop has reported similar trouble with Lithotine. Most shops say they have had no such trouble and LTF's laboratory has not experienced any such difficulty. Actually, it is hard to see why there should be any such trouble with deep-etch plates since the non-blinding lacquer covers the copper image and is not removed by either Lithotine or turpentine.

If your plates show any tendency to blindness or are slow to take ink on the press, consult your supplier regarding a wash-out solvent recommended by him. Some shops omit the solvent wash and wash out plates directly with asphaltum solution. Others use asphaltum solution plus a little press ink for washing out. Both practices are claimed to prevent blinding.

Chapter 23

REMOVING AND ADDING WORK

The removal of dirt specks and unwanted marks from the non-image areas of the plate was done immediately after the plate was cleared (Chapter 17, page 141). There are almost always some clean-up erasures of this type to be made. But occasionally, through some error, it becomes necessary to alter or repair the printing image. And this may involve removing some part of the image, or adding to it, or both. Sometimes the original image must be removed and another put in its place. If the Sensitivity Guide was used as a control in exposure and development, and if it can't appear on the printed sheet, its images must be completely removed from the plate so they won't print.

In this chapter we will discuss methods of removing and adding work areas. Because of differences in properties of the metals, these methods are slightly different for zinc, aluminum and stainless steel.

REMOVING WORK FROM ZINC PLATES

Small areas of unwanted work up to one or two square inches can be erased with a Snake Slip, Scotch Stone, or an abrasive air gun like the Paasche Air Eraser. This is best done in the following steps:

1. Wash the ink or asphaltum off the unwanted work area with naphtha or gasoline.

2. Wash the gum arabic off the immediately surrounding area with water.

3. While the area is wet, polish out the unwanted work with a Snake Slip or Scotch Stone, or abrade it out with an air-eraser. Clean the area with a water sponge and blot it dry.

4. Regrain the area, using a flat-sided glass marble and 240 or 300-mesh aluminum oxide abrasive, or fine graining sand, moistened with hydrochloric acid counter-etch (Chapter 5, page 45). A mushroom-shaped glass bottle stopper is even handier to use than a marble. Wash off the abrasive and blot dry.

5. Desensitize the cleaned area with a good zinc plate etch. Apply the etch twice, and dry it down both times.

6. Wash and re-gum the entire plate.

If the image area to be deleted is *large,* the following method is more practical and effective:

1. Wash the ink or asphaltum off the unwanted work area with naphtha or gasoline.

2. Remove the lacquer with a lacquer solvent such as amyl-acetate or methylethyl ketone. Acetone may be suitable. Your supplier can tell you the best solvent to use. Go over the area several times with the solvent to be sure it is clean, then blot and fan dry.

3. Double-etch the cleaned area, drying down the etch each time.

4. Wash and re-gum the entire plate.

The cellulose gum plate etch (Chapter 20, page 152) is the best for zinc plates and should be used for both small and large areas.

REMOVING WORK FROM ALUMINUM AND STAINLESS STEEL PLATES

To remove work from small areas on aluminum plates, use the same steps as for *small* areas on zinc plates (above), with the following exceptions:

Step 4. Instead of hydrochloric acid counter-etch, use the acetic acid counter-etch (Chapter 5, page 46) or weak nitric acid (one ounce concentrated nitric acid in a quart of water) when you regrain the cleared area. For stainless steel plates use either the hydrochloric acid counter-etch or weak nitric acid.

Step 5. Use a good aluminum plate etch such as the gum-phosphoric etch (see formula in Chapter 20, page 153). You need to apply this etch only once, but dry it down thoroughly.

To remove work from *larger* areas on aluminum and stainless steel plates use the same steps as for *large* areas on zinc plates, except as follows:

Step 3. Before etching the cleaned area, go over it thoroughly with pumice or fine graining abrasive using a piece of flannel or felt dipped in the aluminum plate etch. Scrub with a circular motion. Then wash off the abrasive and make a single application of the etch, drying it down thoroughly.

WORK ADDITIONS IN GENERAL

Solids can be added on deep-etch plates by hand with tusche or deep-etch lacquer. Tints or tones can be added on zinc plates by means of litho crayon, but this is almost never done. To add type matter or halftones, however, it is necessary to repeat the deep-etch platemaking process locally, since these additions can best be made photographically. Broken lettering or lines, and spots in solids can be repaired by scratching through the gum layer with a needle and applying developing ink or press ink directly to the uncovered metal. So the method you use in adding work depends on the type of image to be added.

To add tusche work, you need first to sensitize the area to ink. This means removing every last trace of the desensitizing gum film left on the plate by the etch. However, if you want to replace work that has just been removed, and you have grained the cleaned area with abrasive and counter-etch, you can apply tusche or deep-etch lacquer directly.

Litho crayon comes in sticks. A typical crayon consists of a mixture of wax, tallow, shellac, soap and lampblack. When used to draw on grained plates it can produce tone gradations the values of which depend on how strongly the crayon is rubbed into the grain. Some plates for poster printing are still made by the hand-crayon method. But, since halftones are much more preferable, crayon tones are seldom added on photo-lithographic plates. Zinc plates take crayon work fairly well but on aluminum and stainless steel plates it is quite undependable.

Tusche is made by rubbing litho crayon with water to produce an emulsion having about the consistency of cream. The soap in the crayon emulsifies the wax and grease. Tusche can be applied to the plate with a brush to produce solids, or with a pen to draw lines. But before it can produce a printing image, it must be dried thoroughly on the plate and reacted upon by the plate etch. Otherwise, water would wash it off.

To produce printing images on the plate, tusche work must be treated with an acid to convert the soap into a water-insoluble fatty acid. Assuming, for example, that the soap is sodium oleate, the reaction is as follows:

$$3NaC_{18}H_{34}O_2 \quad + \quad H_3PO_4 \longrightarrow \quad Na_3PO_4 \quad + \quad 3HC_{18}H_{34}O_2$$

Soap	Phosphoric	Sodium	Oleic acid
(sodium oleate)	acid	Phosphate	

When this reaction is complete the tusche is "set". It has attached itself tightly to the metal and can no longer be washed off with water. However, you can't use a plain water solution of acid to produce this reaction since the water would wash or smear the tusche before the acid has had time to react with it. The acid has to be in a viscous medium that doesn't penetrate the tusche layer as rapidly as water does. Fortunately, the application of a plate etch does just what is necessary to produce the printing image. The gum in the etch prevents it from penetrating too fast and washing or smearing the tusche. When the etch is dried down its acid penetrates the layer of tusche and converts its soap into fatty acid. At the same time the etch desensitizes the non-image areas surrounding the added work.

Durable solids can be produced by applying a non-blinding lacquer to freshly counter-etched or deep-etched areas of the plate. This involves a masking technique, since the lacquer is not applied with a brush but must be rubbed down.

Of the three metals, zinc, aluminum and stainless steel, zinc is naturally the most ink receptive. Therefore, direct additions of work with tusche or greasy ink are easiest to make on zinc plates and are more durable than on the other metals. On the other hand, additions of solids with deep-etch lacquer hold equally well on all three metals provided the metal surface has been properly prepared. Since photographic additions (shooting in of halftones or line work) require a deep-etching procedure and the application of deep-etch lacquer, there is essentially no difference in the results obtained with the three metals when additions are "shot in".

ADDING TUSCHE WORK ON ZINC PLATES

The procedure in adding tusche work to completed zinc plates is as follows :

1. Wash the gum off an area considerably larger than that to be occupied by the new work. Do this with a clean water sponge or wad of cotton, and blot the area dry with newsprint or blotting paper.

2. Treat an area larger than the new work with a strong counter-etch (three ounces of concentrated hydrochloric acid to a gallon of water). Apply this with a wad of cotton for about one minute, then blot dry.

3. Counter-etch the area again for one minute, and blot dry. Don't wash off the counter-etch with water.

4. Make the desired additions with tusche to the counter-etched area. Allow the tusche to dry thoroughly.

5. Powder the added work with the 50-50 talc-rosin mixture (Chapter 16, page 137).

6. Double-etch the entire area from which you originally removed the gum with cellulose gum plate etch (Chapter 20, page 153), drying down the etch both times.

7. Wash the gum off the entire plate and re-gum the plate in the regular way (Chapter 21).

The plate image can now be washed out with Lithotine and put under asphaltum (see Chapter 22).

ADDING SOLIDS WITH DEEP-ETCH LACQUER ON ZINC PLATES

To produce a solid with deep-etch lacquer, first remove the gum and counter-etch an area somewhat larger than the solid to be added. Do this in the same way as Steps 1, 2 and 3 in adding tusche work (above). Next, outline the solid with gum arabic solution, using a pen or brush, and paint out all the surrounding area that has been counter-etched also with gum arabic. After the gum has dried thoroughly, apply non-blinding deep-etch lacquer. Rub the lacquer down and dry it (see

Chapter 15), then apply developing ink and powder (Chapter 16). Wash with water to remove the developing ink and gum from the areas around the added solid. Finally, re-etch the area, drying the etch down, wash the entire plate with water and gum it up (Chapters 20 and 21).

ADDING HALFTONES OR TYPE MATTER ON ZINC PLATES

Images containing halftones or type matter have to be added by the regular photographic platemaking procedure. When such additions are necessary, it is usually because of an error in stripping or in photo-composing. Either some wrong copy was shot in, or one positive was shot out of position. In either case the original work must be removed and the correct work added.

When this correction procedure is started, the plate should be under gum, and the image areas under developing ink or rolling-up ink. The image areas should be powdered. To make the correction, the following steps are recommended:

1. Wash the ink off the unwanted work with naphtha or gasoline.

2. Remove the lacquer with a lacquer solvent such as amyl acetate or methylethyl ketone. The supplier of your lacquer can tell you the best solvent to use. Go over the area several times with solvent to be sure it is clean, then blot and fan it dry.

3. Wash the gum off the area and its margins with water.

4. Go over the deleted image area with pumice or fine graining abrasive on a piece of flannel or felt and zinc plate etch, using a circular motion.

5. Place the plate in the whirler, wash off the gum, coat the entire plate with deep-etch coating solution and dry it in the usual way (Chapter 17).

6. Place the positive in the correct position, cover the remainder of the plate with masking paper or foil, and make the exposure in a vacuum printing frame. Alternatively the exposure can be made on the photo-composing machine, in which case the positive should be properly masked to prevent the exposure from overlapping adjacent work areas (Chapter 9).

7. Develop, deep-etch and finish the new image locally, just as you did in making the plate originally (Chapters 10 to 13, 15 and 16).

8. Put the plate under running water and scrub off the new gum stencil (Chapter 17).

9. Remove the residual stencil, and post-treat the new work locally (Chapters 18 and 19).

10. Etch and gum up the entire plate (Chapters 20 and 21).

ADDING TUSCHE WORK ON ALUMINUM AND STAINLESS STEEL PLATES

It is not easy to add tusche work on aluminum plates and make it stick. Special care is required, and even then the work may last for only five or ten thousand impressions. The method requires the same steps as for zinc plates (page 171) with the following exceptions:

1. In steps 2 and 3, instead of the hydrochloric acid counter-etch, use a special counter-etch made as follows:

	Metric Units	U. S. Units
Ammonium Alum,		
$[NH_4Al(SO_4)_2 \cdot 12H_2O]$	7.5 g.	1 avoir. oz. (28 g.)
Hydrofluoric Acid (HF), 48%	7.8 cc.	1 liq. oz. (29 cc.)
Water to make	1000 cc.	1 gallon

Counter-etch the area three times, blotting off the counter-etch after each application. As soon as the plate is dry after the third counter-etching, apply the tusche.

2. In Step 6, use the aluminum plate etch (Chapter 20).

ADDING SOLIDS WITH DEEP-ETCH LACQUER ON ALUMINUM PLATES

Here the method is the same as for zinc plates. (see page 171), except that instead of the hydrochloric acid counter-etch, you should use the hydrofluoric acid-ammonia alum counter-etch. Be sure, of course, to also use the aluminum plate etch for desensitization (Chapter 20).

ADDING HALFTONES OR TYPE MATTER ON ALUMINUM PLATES

Addition or replacement of halftone and type matter on aluminum plates can be done by following the same procedure as for zinc plates with the following exceptions:

1. In Step 7 (page 173) be sure to use the aluminum deep-etching solution (see Chapter 11).

2. Omit Step 9, since post-treatments are of no value on aluminum plates.

3. In Step 10, use the aluminum plate etch (Chapter 20).

ADDING WORK ON STAINLESS STEEL PLATES

In adding solids with tusche or deep-etch lacquer, and in adding or replacing halftones or type matter, on stainless steel plates, follow the same procedure as for aluminum plates.

Chapter 24

BIMETAL, TRI-METAL AND POLY-METAL PLATES

As was stated in the Introduction to this book, on page 5, bimetal plates are composed of two metals, one of which forms the image areas and the other the non-image areas. The metal forming the image areas is selected for its ability to take ink. The metal forming the non-image areas is selected for the ease with which it is wet by water and its ability to be desensitized to ink. To simplify the discussion, these two metals will be referred to as the image metal and the non-image metal, respectively.

Theoretically there are four possible types of bimetal printing plates. These are best described by the methods used to produce them.

TYPE 1. Form an acid-resistant positive image on a plate of an image metal, then electroplate a non-image metal on the remaining areas, and remove the acid resist from the image areas.

TYPE 2. Form a stencil or negative image by means of an acid-resistant coating on a plate of a non-image metal, then electroplate an image metal on the bare image areas, and remove the protective stencil.

TYPE 3. Electroplate an image metal on a plate of a non-image metal; form an acid-resistant positive image on the layer of image metal; etch away the image metal from all except the image areas; then remove the acid resist from the image areas.

175

TYPE 4. Electroplate a non-image metal on a plate of an image metal, or on a plate which carries a surface layer of an image metal; form a stencil or negative image by means of acid-resistant coating on the layer of non-image metal; etch away the non-image metal to lay bare the image metal in the positive image areas; then remove the protective stencil from the non-image areas.

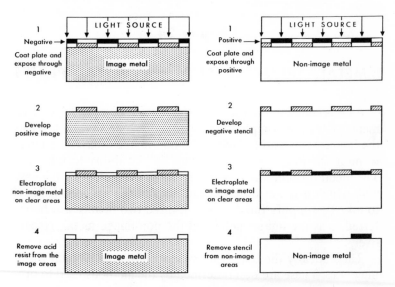

Figure 66. Steps in making a Type-1 bi-metal plate.   Figure 67. Steps in making a Type-2 bi-metal plate.

While all four types have been tried, only Types 3 and 4 have been generally successful. Types 1 and 2 gave trouble because of difficulties in finding photo-resists that would stand up during the electroplating operation, and because of inability to obtain uniform electro-deposits of metal on the non-image or image areas of the plate.

All bimetal plates in general use at the present time are either Type 3 or Type 4. All of them use copper as the image metal, and chromium, aluminum or stainless steel as the non-image metal. One plate, still in the experimental stage, uses iron as the image metal and chromium as the non-image metal.

So-called *tri-metal* and *poly-metal* plates are made from three metals: (a) a base plate of zinc, iron, or aluminum; (b) an electroplated layer of copper (image metal) on the base plate; and (c) an electroplated layer of chromium (non-image metal) on top of the copper layer. However, only the electroplated layers of copper and chromium are affected by the platemaking process and take part in the printing process. So for all practical purposes tri- and poly-metal plates are the same as Type 4 bimetal plates (Figure 69). From here on they will be called bimetal plates. The advantage of using zinc, iron, or aluminum instead of copper as the base plate is that it reduces the weight and cost of plates. Also, plates based on zinc and aluminum are easier to handle, both in platemaking and on the press.

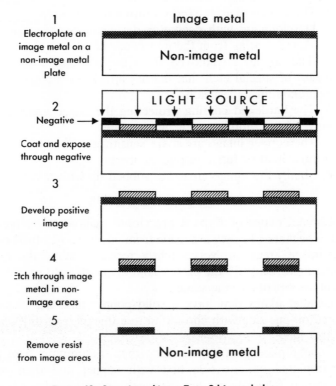

1

Electroplate an image metal on a non-image metal plate

Image metal

Non-image metal

2

Negative →

Coat and expose through negative

LIGHT SOURCE

3

Develop positive image

4

Etch through image metal in non-image areas

5

Remove resist from image areas

Non-image metal

Figure 68. Steps in making a Type-3 bi-metal plate.

TYPE 3 BIMETAL PLATES

Bimetal plates of Type 3 are similar to surface plates (see Introduction page 4) only because (1) they are made from negatives, and (2) because their copper image areas are very slightly raised above the non-image areas. However, the process and materials used in making them are much the same as for deep-etch plates. The two plates of this type available to American lithographers are the Aller plate (copper image on stainless steel) and the Lithengrave plate (copper image on aluminum). The Lithengrave plate was largely developed by LTF.

The steps in making a Type 3 bimetal plate are as follows:

1. The copper coating of the plate is cleaned by counter-etching with a dilute acid.

2. The cleaned plate is coated in the usual way with regular deep-etch coating solution and dried.

3. The coated plate is exposed through a negative.

4. Development with deep-etch developer removes the unhardened coating from the non-image areas.

5. The copper is removed from the non-image areas by means of special etch that doesn't attack the stainless steel or aluminum underneath.

6. The hardened coating protecting the image areas is removed by scrubbing under warm water.

7. The copper image areas are sensitized to ink with weak sulfuric acid or ferric nitrate solution.

8. Finally the image areas are rubbed up with ink.

TYPE 4 BIMETAL PLATES

Bimetal plates of Type 4 are closely related to deep-etch plates because (1) they are made from positives, (2) their copper image areas are very slightly recessed below the non-image areas, and (3) the process and materials used in making them are essentially the same.

Bimetal plates that have a solid copper base are electroplated on one side with chromium to a thickness of .00005 to .00007 inch.

Bimetal plates that have a zinc, iron, or aluminum base are electroplated on one side first with copper and then with chromium. These layers are extremely thin, the copper being

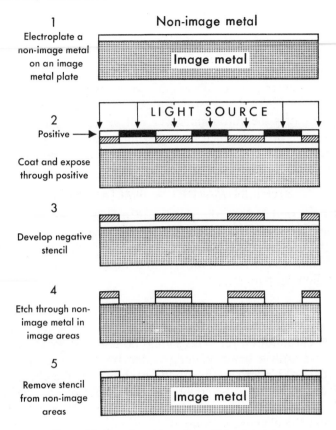

Figure 69. Steps in making a Type-4 bi-metal plate.

from about .00001 to .001 inch thick and the chromium being from .00005 to .00007 inch thick. All of the suppliers can furnish plates with zinc as the base metal. One or more can furnish plates with iron or aluminum as the base metal. Which base metal is used depends on the lithographer's preference. Iron is much stronger than zinc and won't stretch on the press or tear out at the clamp edges. Aluminum has about the same strength as zinc but is less than half its weight. It is also more brittle and free from permanent stretch.

Suppliers can furnish bimetal plates either grained or ungrained. The ungrained plates are made by electroplating ungrained base plates. To make grained bimetal plates, the base plates are first grained in the usual way (Chapter 4) and then electroplated with copper and chromium.

The chromium layer on bimetal plates is not like the bright chrome plating on your automobile trim. Instead it has a dull matte appearance, even on ungrained plates. This is necessary to make it carry water properly during printing. When you receive plates the chromium layer will be under gum, that is, it will have been gummed up with gum arabic. The gum layer is necessary to prevent the surface from being scratched and to protect it from contamination by dirt or grease.

STEPS IN MAKING A BIMETAL PLATE

As we said before, the process of making a bimetal plate of the type under discussion is essentially the same as that for making a deep-etch plate on a single metal. There are a few important differences, however, and these will be shown in the following paragraphs.

Plate Treatment Prior to Coating

Bimetal plates come with a protective coating of gum arabic on the chromium layer. This should be removed by scrubbing the plate with a brush under running water before applying the coating. Under certain conditions, however, the chromium surface may need to be counter-etched or chemically cleaned after the gum is removed. Consult your supplier regarding this and the chemicals required.

Coating and Drying the Plate

The regular bichromated gum deep-etch coating solution is used on bimetal plates to produce the light-sensitive coating (see Chapter 7, page 61). For grained plates, use the full strength coating, the same as for grained zinc or aluminum plates. For smooth bimetal plates, reduce the Baumé of the coating solution to about 12° with water. Very thin coatings such as are used on ungrained zinc and aluminum plates (Chapter 7) won't work on bimetal plates.

The method of coating and drying grained bimetal plates is exactly the same as that for grained deep-etch plates as described in Chapter 7. The same troubles can occur, so the same precautions and controls should be used. For ungrained bimetal plates, the whirling speed should be increased to 60 or 75 rpm.

The light sensitivity of the dried coating on a bimetal plate is affected by the six variables described in Chapter 8, and these should be controlled in the same way as in making deep-etch plates.

Exposing the Plate

The equipment for exposing the plate and the methods of controlling exposure are the same for bimetal as for deep-etch plates (see Chapter 9). There are, however, certain differences in the materials used.

Good, sharp positives are required. But for the best results, halftone positives should be made a little "higher" than for deep-etch plates. By "higher" we mean that all tones should be lighter or sharper. The reason for this is that, in etching through the chromium layer after the image has been developed, there is a sidewise etching that enlarges the dots. So, to produce the same tone values on a bimetal plate as on a deep-etch plate, the halftone dots on the positive must be slightly smaller. If you should use the same positives as for deep-etch, the half-tones would be too heavy. The LTF Sensitivity Guide should be used since it is important to control the exposure.

Bimetal plates require a special strong etching solution to bite through the chromium layer and bare the copper in the image areas. This etching solution has a greater tendency to penetrate the gum stencil than do the deep-etching solutions. For this reason, the gum stencil may need to be harder on bimetal plates. This greater hardness can be obtained by increasing the exposure. It is best to follow the supplier's instructions in this regard.

Stopping Out Before Development

Unexposed borders and other unwanted areas that can easily be seen after the plate has been exposed can either be stopped out with shellac or lacquer, or exposed out. These steps are the same as those described in Chapter 13, page 124. Minor imperfections such as dust spots and tape marks that are not easily seen at this point should be stopped out after development.

Developing the Plate

The developing solution and method of development are in every way the same for bimetal plates as for aluminum deep-etch plates (see Chapter 10). There is, of course, no frothing during development as in the case of zinc plates. Use of the LTF Sensitivity Guide is essential in securing proper development.

Stopping Out After Development

The stopping out of minor imperfections such as dust spots, joints and tape marks with deep-etch coating solution should be done after development and before etching through the chromium layer. If it were done after the etching, these unwanted areas would appear on the finished plate as bared copper. And, while copper can be desensitized, its desensitization doesn't last very long. So, if there are unwanted areas that can't be stopped out before development, wash the plate with anhydrous alcohol immediately after development and dry it. Then stop out the unwanted areas with deep-etch coating solution, dry, and give the plate a flat exposure to an arc light as described in Chapter 13, page 126. After this supplementary light exposure, you can proceed to etch away the chromium in the image areas.

Etching Through the Chromium Layer

Etching through the chromium layer to bare the copper in the image areas corresponds to the deep-etching operation described in Chapter 11. To do this, a special chromium etch is required. A suitable etch and the instructions for its use can be obtained from the firm that supplies your bimetal plates.

LTF has developed a non-fuming chromium etch for bimetal plates. It is covered by U.S. Patent No. 2,599,914, issued June 10, 1952.

Non-Fuming Chromium Etch

	Metric Units	U. S. Units
Aluminum Chloride ($AlCl_3$) Solution, 32° Bé	750 cc.	3 quarts
Zinc Chloride ($ZnCl_2$), Technical	630 g.	5¼ lbs.
Phosphoric Acid (H_3PO_3), 85%	40 cc.	5 liq. oz. (148 cc.)

Instructions for preparing this etch are given in the Appendix, page 218. This etch is applied in much the same way as the deep-etching solution is applied on deep-etch plates. The etching is stopped as soon as the copper image is completely exposed.

The etching time will vary somewhat depending on the thickness of the chromium layer. It is usually faster if the chromium surface of the plate was counter-etched or chemically cleaned just before the plate was coated (see page 180).

Cleaning the Copper Image Areas

Removing the chromium etch from the copper image areas is done by washing the plate three or four times with anhydrous alcohol in exactly the same way as cleaning the deep-etched image areas, described in Chapter 12.

Sensitizing the Copper Image Areas to Ink

Since the image areas of the bimetal plate are copper, they are easily made ink receptive. They don't require the coating of non-blinding lacquer recommended for zinc and aluminum deep-etch plates. Once the copper takes ink properly, the image will not blind readily during the normal printing process.

After the copper image areas have been washed with alcohol, they are immediately coated with a thin film of asphaltum. This may be straight asphaltum (see Chapter 22) or asphaltum containing a fatty acid like oleic acid. From here on the treatment can be varied and it is best to follow the recommendations of your plate supplier. One procedure is to apply the asphaltum, remove the gum stencil, then rub up the image areas with ink. Another procedure is to follow the asphaltum with an application of developing ink, powder the ink with powdered asphaltum or Dragons Blood (a resin used as an acid resist in photoengraving) and then remove the gum stencil. Still another method is to omit the alcohol wash after the etching and immediately remove the gum stencil; then treat the copper image areas with dilute ferric nitrate solution (one ounce ferric nitrate [$Fe(NO_3)_3 \cdot 9H_2O$] to one quart of water) and rub them up with ink.

Removing the Gum Stencil

The gum stencil is removed by soaking the plate in warm water and then scrubbing with a bristle brush in the same way as for deep-etch plates (see Chapter 18).

Desensitizing the Non-Image Areas

Since the non-image areas on bimetal plates are chromium which is very easily desensitized, there is no need to remove the residual stencil or to give these areas any sort of post-treatment. So, immediately after scrubbing off the gum stencil you can apply a desensitizing plate etch (Chapter 20), and gum up the plate (Chapter 21). Any gum arabic or cellulose gum plate etch gives good results. The instructions and precautions given for these operations on deep-etch plates apply also to bimetal plates.

Removing and Adding Work

As in the case of deep-etch plates, work can be removed from or added to finished bimetal plates. Consult the supplier of your plates about this as he will have the most up-to-date methods.

Small spots that show up on the finished plate can be removed by polishing with a snake slip or pencil eraser. Even though this abrasion bares the copper, the areas can be desensitized with a plate etch and should stay clean for some time. However, a more permanent repair can be made by electroplating chromium on the copper spots. This can be done by applying chromic acid solution and using a pencil- or spatula-type electrode. Consult your plate supplier about this equipment.

Broken lettering or lines, and spots in solids can be repaired by scratching through the chromium layer with a needle, and applying ink.

If it should be necessary to remove one image area and replace it with another, this can also be done. The procedure is as follows:

1. Wash all ink off the area with gasoline or naphtha.

2. Paint or stage out the surrounding area with stop-out shellac or lacquer so it will be protected.

3. Apply chromium etch (see page 182) to remove all the chromium in the bare area.

4. Wash thoroughly with alcohol to remove the chromium etch. The alcohol will also remove the shellac or lacquer from the surrounding area.

5. Scrub the bared copper with fine pumice and water, using a felt pad, to slightly roughen the copper. Wash off the pumice, and dry.

6. Use a roller-type electrode and chromic acid solution to replate chromium on the bared copper area. Your supplier can tell you where to get the equipment.

7. Wash with water to remove the chromic acid.

8. Apply deep-etch coating, shoot in the new work, develop, etch and finish locally in the same way you made the plate originally.

Chapter 25

TROUBLES IN DEEP-ETCH PLATEMAKING

1. Plate Coating Is Not Uniform

CAUSE A: The coating solution was made with ropy or stringy gum.

REMEDY: Select gum arabic carefully. Use the bag method for dissolving it. (See Appendix, page 209.)

CAUSE B: The coating solution contains air bubbles. These leave pinholes or comets in the coating.

REMEDY: Avoid beating air into the coating solution. Remove any air bubbles by straining the solution through damp cheesecloth. Don't keep the coating solution in a refrigerator. Pour the coating solution onto the plate carefully in one continuous movement. (See Chapter 7, page 66 and Appendix, page 210.)

CAUSE C: Counter-etching the plate did not remove all the grease.

REMEDY: Wash the coating off, re-counter-etch and re-coat the plate. (See Chapter 7, page 67.)

CAUSE D: The coating contained solid particles such as undissolved dye, fibers, or dirt.

REMEDY: Filter the dye solution more carefully. Re-strain coating solution. Be sure no lint adheres to the counter-etched plate.

CAUSE E: Dust in the air or particles dropping from the ceiling or from a dirty whirler.

REMEDY: If the air is dusty, keep the whirler closed, and dry the plate without air circulation. Paint or cover ceiling to prevent dropping of particles. Clean the whirler thoroughly every day.

CAUSE F: Sediment in the water used in rinsing and flooding the plate.

REMEDY: Install a filter in the water system.

2. Plate Requires Prolonged Development

CAUSE A: Coating has hardened in the unexposed image areas due to dark reaction. Generally happens only in hot, humid weather.

REMEDY: Air condition your platemaking room or at least put in a dehumidifier. Try to produce a thicker coating by slowing down the whirler speed. Cut down the time between coating and development as much as possible. In an emergency, try reducing your developer Baumé 1 or 2 degrees with water. (See Chapter 10, page 110.)

CAUSE B: The Baumé of the developer is too high for the plate temperature.

REMEDY: Adjust the Baumé to a lower value (see Chapter 10, page 110.)

CAUSE C: Coating in the image areas has been hardened by exposure to light.

REMEDY: Protect the coated plate at all times from all-over light exposure. Do your stopping out as quickly as possible, especially in hot, humid weather.

3. Plate Develops Too Fast

CAUSE: The Baumé of the developer is too low for the plate temperature.

REMEDY: Use a developer with a higher Baumé (see Chapter 10, page 110.). Use the stabilized developer.

4. Halftone Dots Are Broken — Lack Sharpness

CAUSE A: Plate grain too coarse.

REMEDY: Use a finer grain. Fine grained plates, properly etched, will carry water on the press as well as coarse grained plates.

CAUSE B: Development has not been complete.

REMEDY: Adjust developer to clear the work areas two to three minutes after first application. Use Sensitivity Guide. If clearing goes to a step below 9 in three minutes, increase the light exposure. (See Chapter 10, page 112.)

CAUSE C: Too much dark reaction.

REMEDY: Cut down the time between coating and development as much as you can. If you use heat in the whirler, don't let the plate get hotter than 110° F. Don't leave plate in the warm whirler longer than necessary. (See Chapter 7, page 69.)

CAUSE D: Camera positives with excessive halation.

REMEDY: Have better camera positives made, or make contact positives. Avoid excessive dot etching of positives.

5. Excessive Dirt Spots That Have To Be Polished Out

CAUSE A: Pinholes due to air bubbles in the coating.

REMEDY: Avoid beating air into the gum solution or when mixing the coating solution. Strain the coating solution. Remove bubbles from solution before pouring on plate. Hold container close to the plate while pouring and pour steadily in one motion. (See Chapter 7, page 66 and Appendix, page 210.)

CAUSE B: Specks of material that fall on the plate before coating is dry.

REMEDY: Keep whirler absolutely clean, especially the lid.

CAUSE C: Specks of dirt on positives.

REMEDY: Have camera department supply clean positives. Prevent dust on positives.

6. The Coating Doesn't Dry Hard—Remains Tacky

CAUSE: Excessive moisture in the coating when the relative humidity is high (above 70%).

REMEDY: The best remedy is to prevent this trouble by air conditioning your platemaking room. If this isn't possible, there are certain other things you can do.

If you use a printing frame, you can take plates out of the

whirler while still warm and expose them right away. Don't allow any time for the coating to become stabilized. If you have good sharp positives, you should not have any trouble. Increase the exposure if necessary.

If you use a photo-composing machine, you can apply wax, lacquer, or thin asphaltum to your plates while they are still warm from the whirler to keep the coating from becoming tacky (see Chapter 7, page 70). This will prevent sticking of positives and gasket to the plate. Or, you can have multiple positives made and stripped on a vinylite sheet so you can expose the plate in a printing frame. The latter method is best for plates that would have to stay on the photo-composing machine longer than about four hours.

7. Fine, "Spider-Web" Scum Develops in the Non-Image Areas of the Finished Plate

CAUSE: Shrinkage cracks in the coating due to excessive dryness.

REMEDY: Here again, air conditioning is the best remedy. If it isn't possible, make your coating thinner. You can do this either by speeding up the whirler or by thinning the coating solution with water.

If this does not help, try adding up to two ounces of glycerine to a gallon of coating solution. Avoid bending the plate more than necessary.

8. Fine, Over-All Scum Shows on the Non-Image Areas of the Finished Plate

CAUSE: The deep-etch coating was too thin, or too moist due to high humidity. It was penetrated over the grain peaks by the developer and deep-etching solution. This is "penetration" scum and cannot be gummed or etched out.

REMEDIES: Make a new plate, using a thicker coating. If your developer works too fast, increase its Baumé. Use a finer plate grain.

9. Scum Develops in Areas Where Masking Tape Contacted the Coating

CAUSE: Use of a masking tape that attracts moisture in humid weather.

REMEDY: Use a masking tape that has a plastic or cellulose acetate base. Tapes made on a cellophane base contain glycerine or a similar material that attracts moisture.

10. Plates Under Developing Ink Can't Be Washed Out

CAUSE A: Gum has dried over all or part of the work. This keeps the Lithotine or turpentine from contacting and dissolving the ink.

REMEDY: Wash the plate with water to remove the gum; while plate is wet, wash out the ink with Lithotine; rub up or roll up the image with ink (see Chapter 21, page 160). On future plates, apply a heavier film of developing ink that will repel the gum better. Use greater care in gumming up.

CAUSE B: Developing ink has dried on the work areas so that Lithotine or turpentine will not dissolve it.

REMEDY: Wash the plate with a solvent for dried ink, such as half and half xylol and ethyl acetate or butyl acetate. When the ink has been removed, put the plate under asphaltum. Use a developing ink that won't dry hard on the plate.

11. Scum Specks on Aluminum Plates (Oxidation Scum)

CAUSE A: Use of a counter-etch such as hydrochloric or hydrofluoric acid that removed the protective aluminum oxide film on the plate in spots.

REMEDY: Use only acetic acid or citric acid counter-etch (see Chapter 5, page 48).

CAUSE B: Gum arabic solution preserved with a mercury salt.

REMEDY: Use only carbolic acid (phenol) or other mercury-free compound for preserving gum solutions (see Appendix, page 209).

CAUSE C: Imbedded graining abrasive.

REMEDY: Inspect the plate grain carefully before coating the plate. Discard plates that show imbedded abrasive after being counter-etched (see Chapter 5, page 49).

Chapter 26

HEALTH AND SAFETY

IN DEEP-ETCH PLATEMAKING

The efficient operation of a lithographic plant depends on good equipment and its proper arrangement, but, above all, on the efficiency of the men who carry out the operations necessary to produce its products. And to be efficient, these men must be able to work under conditions that promote their health and safety. When time is lost due to ill health, or accident, it is not only a matter of discomfort and expense to the individual, but the efficiency of the department in which he works, and even of the entire plant, is impaired.

The maintenance of safe working conditions is therefore the responsibility of both the front office and operating personnel. Management should provide the necessary safeguards, and the workers themselves should make a habit of safe practices and good personal hygiene. It is to their personal advantage to do so as well as to that of the organization as a whole.

The things that contribute most to safe operation in deep-etch platemaking are good housekeeping, fire prevention, proper handling of chemicals, proper handling of glass and metal plates, personal hygiene, and the safe operation of equipment. They will be considered in that order.

GOOD HOUSEKEEPING

No one needs to be told that there is a direct relationship between cleanliness and order in the platemaking department and the number and quality of plates produced. And, in addi-

191

tion, the men are happier in clean, orderly surroundings. They are free from annoyances and irritation that make personal relations difficult and prevent smooth, cooperative effort.

There are many things that can cause annoyances and irritation. If the whirler isn't cleaned regularly, if paint is flaking off the ceiling, or if dust from the floor or equipment is stirred up, coated plates will be full of comets and will have to be re-coated. If the floor is wet so that someone slips or falls while carrying a glass positive or a plate, or if an obstruction causes him to stumble, it may mean an expensive re-make. This is not only costly, but also aggravating. If developing and deep-etching pads are not cleaned properly after each use, the next plate on which they are used may be ruined. If tools or utensils are misplaced, time and energy are wasted hunting for them. These are simply examples. There are many others.

By keeping rooms, benches and equipment clean, there is less chance for contact with chemicals which might cause skin irritation and dermatitis. Spilled chemicals should therefore be cleaned up thoroughly so that there can be no accidental skin contact, or contamination of pads or sponges which in turn might damage a plate.

Good housekeeping is everybody's business. It is not only necessary to have a set of rules; it is also necessary that everybody who works in the department be alert to prevent conditions that might cause personal injury or even annoyance to fellow workers. Have a place for everything and keep everything in its place.

Deposit used paper wipes and newsprint sheets in waste containers, and see that they are disposed of daily.

Use self-closing metal containers for used rags.

Keep cleaning solvents in safety cans. Keep anhydrous alcohol cans tightly capped or stoppered at all times.

Keep containers of chemicals in cupboards or on shelves where there is no danger of breakage.

Dispose of broken glass immediately before it can injure anyone.

Clean equipment, benches, tables and floors daily to prevent accumulations of dust and chemicals. In sweeping floors use oiled sawdust to prevent flying dust.

Keep walls and ceilings painted, and have them washed periodically to prevent dust accumulations.

By doing these things you will not only improve the quality and efficiency of your work, you will also improve the morale of the department.

FIRE PREVENTION

Everyone should be fire-prevention conscious. A serious fire would mean loss of jobs.

While good housekeeping is a very important factor in fire prevention, there are hazards connected with the handling of paper, rags, solvents and chemicals that are necessary to the platemaking process. Everyone in the department should know these hazards and how to deal with them to prevent fires, and how to control a fire if necessary.

To begin with, smoking, and particularly the disposal of matches, cigarettes and cigar butts, and pipe ashes can be serious fire hazards. Even if the building is fireproof, and if insurance regulations permit smoking on the job, workmen should know where and when it is safe to smoke. Matches, cigarette and cigar butts, and pipe ashes should never be thrown into waste cans along with paper or rags, or on the floor. Ash trays or other safe containers should be provided for this purpose.

Since you have to handle inflammable solvents you should learn to respect them and handle them safely. A solvent fire could not only destroy the building, but could cause severe personal injury or death. Fire prevention in the platemaking department requires that the following precautions be observed:

1. Rooms where solvents are used should be well ventilated to prevent dangerous accumulations of solvent vapors.

2. If possible, use solvents and alcohols only under ventilating hoods.

3. Don't keep more than five gallons of any solvent or alcohol in the department. Larger quantities should be stored outside the building in a special fireproof storage space. Underwriters' rules regarding solvents may vary in different localities. Be sure you know what they are and follow them.

4. Keep only small amounts of solvents at your work place, and then only in approved safety cans. Two-quart cans are usually large enough for convenience.

5. Avoid spilling solvents. The vapors are heavy and can flow along the floor where they might be ignited and flash back.

6. Bottles of inflammable liquids, especially turpentine, should not be placed in direct sunlight or near artificial heat. This has been known to cause explosions and fire.

7. Don't smoke while you are handling inflammable liquids, or in areas where others are doing so. Don't smoke in areas where such liquids are stored. These liquids include gasoline, naphtha, anhydrous alcohols, isopropyl alcohol, copperizing solution, stop-out shellac or lacquer, deep-etch lacquer, and developing ink.

8. Place rags and paper wipes that are used with solvents in approved self-closing safety containers.

9. Be especially careful not to spill concentrated nitric acid. In contact with paper or rags it can cause spontaneous combustion. Wood, if saturated with nitric acid, becomes more easily ignited.

10. Place used carbons from arc lamps in metal containers to cool off.

11. If you have a wood floor, place metal plates under arc lamps to catch hot sparks from carbons.

If, in spite of precautions, a fire should break out, all operators in the department should know the following things:

1. How to notify the fire department.

2. The location of fire extinguishers and how to use them.

3. The fact that water should not be used directly to put out a solvent fire. One or more buckets of sand, or a carbon dioxide fire extinguisher, should be on hand for this purpose.

4. How to escape from the building if necessary.

HANDLING OF CHEMICALS

In Chapter 3 we listed all the necessary formulas for deep-etch platemaking solutions and discussed the properties of the various chemicals used in making them. While precautions in handling these chemicals were stressed, they are important enough to bear some repetition here. Also some chemicals that were not discussed in Chapter 3 are used in a few shops and need to be mentioned. The containers in which chemicals are received will also be discussed from the standpoint of safety. And, since accidents can happen, the precautionary use of personal protective equipment will be stressed.

The hazards connected with the handling of chemicals should first be classified and defined.

POISONS. The word "POISON" on a label means that the contents of the container can cause death if even a small amount is swallowed. However, many chemicals not labeled "poison" are toxic, meaning that they would make you sick if you swallowed them, if you breathed too much of their vapors, or if you absorbed too much of them through the skin. So, as we have said before, treat all chemicals with reasonable caution. Never eat while you are handling chemicals, and always wash your hands thoroughly before you eat.

CORROSIVE MATERIALS. In connection with personal safety, a corrosive chemical is one that attacks and damages the skin or mucous membrane. Its action is to kill the cells in much the same way as scalding or burning. If the corrosive action goes deep enough, the burn can be very painful. If the corrosive action is only superficial, it irritates the skin and makes it more susceptible to dermatitis.

IRRITANTS. An irritant is a material that damages the natural protective elements in the skin. Irritants include solvents that remove fats from the skin and cause it to become dry or tender. Mildly corrosive chemicals can also act as irritants.

SENSITIZERS. Any material that damages the natural protective elements of the skin so that it can be invaded by the spores of fungi or other things that may cause dermatitis is called a sensitizer. Once the skin has become "sensitive", there is no known permanent cure. The symptoms of dermatitis are swelling, thickening and cracking of the skin, and the development of small, watery blisters. This is accompanied by severe itching and discomfort.

EXPLOSIVES. Ordinarily, one thinks of explosives as materials like gunpowder or dynamite. In this sense, there are no explosives used in deep-etch platemaking. But explosions can be caused by the improper handling of certain chemicals, and their results can be very harmful.

Having thus defined the hazards, let's consider the individual deep-etch chemicals that require special care in handling.

Poisons

All chemicals should be handled with care. However, some are more dangerous than others and, to handle them safely, you have to know something about them.

Sodium and potassium cyanides are deadly poisons. A few milligrams, if swallowed, would kill a man almost instantly. Enough could be absorbed through a cut in the skin to cause serious illness. However, the greatest danger in using them is that in pouring their solutions in a drain they may come in contact with an acid. This would liberate a deadly gas, Hydrocyanic Acid, (HCN), the breathing of which could be fatal.

The use of cyanides is never necessary in deep-etch platemaking, and it is best not to have them in the shop.

Mercury, copper, lead and zinc salts are all poisons. But only copper and zinc salts are recommended for deep-etch platemaking. These give off no poisonous vapors and are not readily absorbed through the skin.

Oxalic acid is a violent poison if swallowed. It is used in some shops as a 5-percent solution for removing scum from aluminum plates. Properly used, it offers no health hazard.

Concentrated hydrofluoric acid gives off a poisonous vapor, and care should be taken not to breathe it. But in the weak concentration used in Brunak solution, there are practically no fumes, and no special precautions are necessary.

Hydrochloric acid and ammonia have such pungent and irritating odors that you couldn't breathe harmful amounts of their vapors without a lot of discomfort.

Concentrated nitric acid also has a pungent and irritating odor that prevents unintentional breathing. The main danger from nitric acid, however, comes when it is spilled on paper, rags, sawdust or other oxidizable materials. In this case it may give off brown fumes of nitrogen oxides (NO_2 and N_2O_3) that are extremely harmful to the lungs. Avoid breathing such fumes at all cost. In case of an accident, put on a gas mask, then flood the material with water. If no gas mask is available, call the fire department. Prevent accidental spilling of nitric acid by careful handling.

The vapors of solvents are all more or less toxic. However, only those of benzene (benzol) and carbon tetrachloride are dangerous under ordinary use conditions. The main danger comes from continued (day after day) use of these solvents, since their effect is cumulative. They should never be used in platemaking.

Other solvents, such as gasoline, benzine (naphtha), turpentine, Lithotine, and the alcohols can be safely used in well ventilated rooms.

None of the other chemicals you will use are considered to be dangerous poisons. Most of them are toxic, however, and should be handled with care.

Corrosive Materials

Of all the liquid concentrated acids, sulfuric and nitric acids are the most corrosive. Concentrated phosphoric acid comes next, followed by hydrofluoric acid, hydrochloric acid, and acetic acid. If these acids come in contact with the skin, wash them off immediately. If you should spill them on your clothing, take off the clothing immediately and wash any acid off your skin.

Iron perchloride and, to a lesser extent, the other chloride and nitrate salt solutions you will use are mildly corrosive to the skin. This applies also to the developing, deep-etching, and copperizing solutions used in deep-etch platemaking. Avoid skin contact with them by wearing rubber gloves. Even though they may not cause painful burns, they can irritate the skin and make it more susceptible to dermatitis.

Caustic soda and caustic potash, often called lye, are sometimes used in cleaning plates, but are not recommended. Their solutions are extremely corrosive to the skin. In case you should use them, wear rubber gloves and goggles. A drop of lye splashed in your eye could cause blindness.

Irritants

All of the corrodants mentioned above are skin irritants. But whether they are corrosive or simply irritating to the skin depends on their concentration and how long they remain before you wash them off.

All of the solvents, benzene, carbon tetrachloride, gasoline, benzine, turpentine, Lithotine, and the alcohols are, to some extent, skin irritants. They remove protective fatty materials from the skin and cause it to become dry and tender. Turpentine is the most irritating and its use should be avoided if possible. Some people are allergic to turpentine and develop dermatitis when they use it.

While ammonium bichromate seems to be only mildly irritating to the skin, it is also a sensitizer. Men who are allergic to it quickly develop dermatitis. Great care should be taken by all not to allow it to come in contact with, or remain on, the skin. This applies particularly to Cronak solution, Brunak solution, deep-etch coating solution, and plate etches that contain bichromate.

Sensitizers

While all skin irritants could possibly also be sensitizers, this term is used to classify those materials which most frequently cause dermatitis. Actually, very little is known about sensitization. We do know from experience, however, that dermatitis occurs most frequently among men who handle bichromates and turpentine. Lithographers call it "bichromate poisoning". Painters call it "turpentine" rash. About one man in ten is susceptible or allergic to these materials and his skin quickly develops an itchy rash. One or two men in a hundred develop a similar rash from handling petroleum solvents, such as gasoline and benzine. Unfortunately there is no known preventive for those who are susceptible except to avoid these materials.

Most lithographers are able to handle bichromate and turpentine with no apparent ill effects. But now and then a man who has worked with one or both of these materials without trouble, sometimes for years, suddenly becomes sensitized and his hands break out with dermatitis. From then on he is susceptible and little or nothing can be done to help him. Usually he must change his job so he can avoid handling the sensitizing materials.

So, in view of the trouble that bichromate and turpentine can cause, all platemakers are advised to handle them with care. Avoid getting them on your skin, and if this happens accidentally or unavoidably, wash them off as quickly as possible with soap and water.

Explosives

A dangerous explosion can be caused by adding water to concentrated sulfuric acid. The reason for this is that a great deal of heat is generated—enough to produce a sudden evolution of steam. This would throw the strong acid in your face and over your body causing serious burns and damaging your eyesight. Unless someone quickly doused you with water, you could be permanently blinded or disfigured.

When making solutions such as Cronak with sulfuric acid, therefore, always add the concentrated acid to the water—not water to sulfuric acid. Also add the acid slowly while stirring the water. This method is perfectly safe.

Caustic soda or caustic potash (lye) can also cause explosions if they aren't dissolved properly. Never remove the top from a can of lye, or punch holes in the can top, and then place the can in water to let the lye dissolve. A lot of heat will be generated in the can and the steam formed will blow it up, throwing lye over anyone who happens to be near. This could cause blindness and serious burns.

The proper way to dissolve lye is to open the can and pour its contents carefully into water that is being stirred.

Certain solvents, particularly turpentine, can become explosive. Direct sunlight on a bottle of turpentine causes the formation of explosive "peroxides." Keep turpentine and other inflammable solvents only in cans.

As everyone knows, alcohol and certain petroleum solvents, particularly gasoline, give off vapors that can form explosive mixtures with air. The danger from explosion, however, is usually minor compared to that of the fire which usually follows. This hazard was previously discussed under the heading, "Fire Prevention", Page 193.

Chemical Containers

The containers in which chemicals are received by lithographic shops depend on both the nature of the material and the quantity. Materials that are corrosive or hygroscopic (absorb moisture from the atmosphere) and very pure chemicals are shipped in glass bottles. Solid chemicals that are non-corrosive and non-hygroscopic are mostly shipped in cartons.

Corrosive liquids, such as sulfuric acid, nitric acid and hydrochloric acid, in the quantities used by most platemakers, are received in standard 2½ liter glass-stoppered bottles. Hydrofluoric acid comes in wax or plastic bottles since it attacks glass. Iron perchloride solutions are usually purchased in returnable five-gallon glass carboys (bottles enclosed in a wooden box). Carboys are also used for larger quantities of sulfuric, nitric, and hydrochloric acids when so ordered.

One of the main hazards in handling chemicals is therefore the accidental breakage of glass containers. But by taking ordinary care, breakage can be prevented. Here are a few rules to follow:

1. When you handle glass bottles, be sure your hands are clean and dry. Wear rubber or neoprene gloves when you are handling bottles of strong acids, and be sure the gloves are dry.

2. If you should have to handle carboys, move them only by means of a truck. Don't move them unless they are stoppered. Be sure the box is in good shape.

3. When pouring acid or iron perchloride from a carboy, use a tilting cradle designed for the purpose. Wear rubber gloves and goggles. The safest way to remove acid from a carboy is to use a plastic suction pump designed for the purpose.

4. Wash out empty carboys before returnnig them. Any acid left in them is a hazard to the trucker.

5. LTF formulas specify 99% acetic acid. Bottles of it should be handled with the same care as the other corrosive acids. Glacial acetic acid (100%) freezes at about 60°F. When it freezes, it expands and will break the bottle. Be sure to order only the 99% strength.

6. Store bottles of acids in separate cabinets from other chemicals and solvents.

7. If you purchase prepared deep-etch chemicals from a supplier, these will come in one-gallon glass jugs. It is well to have a separate cabinet for them. However, none of them will be as hazardous to handle as the concentrated acids already discussed.

8. Don't use glass bottles for inflammable solvents, lacquers, asphaltum or developing inks. Solvents should be kept in cans, preferably safety cans. Lacquer, asphaltum and developing inks come in metal containers.

9. Under no conditions should bottles of inflammable liquids, particularly turpentine, be exposed to direct sunlight or stored near artificial heat sources. This has been known to cause them to explode and result in disastrous fires.

With the above knowledge, and proper care, all the chemicals you will have to use can be handled safely. Carelessness should not be tolerated.

HANDLING GLASS PLATES AND GLASSWARE

Wherever glass is handled, there is the hazard of breakage which, in addition to destruction of the glass, exposes the worker to possible injury from glass cuts which can be very serious. To avoid the breakage of glass plates (usually positives) here are a few simple rules to follow:

1. Never carry glass plates under your arms. Carry them at your side, not in front, so that if you should trip, the glass will fall to the side where you can't fall on it.

2. Lift glass plates by gripping the top front corner with left hand and bottom rear corner with right hand.

3. Get help in handling larger plates.

4. Before picking up a glass plate, inspect it for imperfections. Its edges and corners should be rounded off. Cracked glass should be discarded in a special receptacle where it can do no damage.

5. Use a truck or dolly to move plates into or out of your department.

6. Wear rubber gloves, snug sleeves, a rubber apron, and goggles when you have to clean plates with corrosive chemicals such as nitric acid.

7. Keep glass plates in enclosed stalls or racks where they can't be bumped into accidentally.

8. Never stand under a plate when you remove it from a stall. A glass chip might fall in your face or eye.

One platemaker solved the problem of injuries from glass breakage by keeping all plates in envelopes, regardless of size, when not in actual use. If one breaks, the pieces remain in the envelope with little chance of injury to the person handling it.

The only chemical or laboratory glassware usually handled by the platemaker are graduates, hydrometer cylinders, Baumé hydrometers and thermometers. Beakers and glass jars are used in relatively few shops. Breakage can occur due to rough handling or dropping. Unless it is of "Pyrex" glass, any vessel is likely to break if it is filled with hot water when it is cold. And broken glass can cause serious cuts. So laboratory glassware is a hazard unless it is handled carefully.

PERSONAL HYGIENE

By developing good personal hygiene habits and wearing protective equipment consistent with the nature and degree of hazard, deep-etch platemakers can be as safe from personal injury as workers in any industrial occupation.

By good personal hygiene we mean wearing clean clothing at all times, and avoiding skin contact with chemicals that are poisonous, corrosive or irritant, or which, like bichromate and turpentine, tend to sensitize the skin and cause dermatitis. If you make a habit of doing this, your job can be a clean and healthy one. However, as we said before, about one person in ten is naturally sensitive to bichromate and such a person simply can't handle it or solutions that contain it. The others need have no fear of sensitization as long as they protect their skin properly.

Good housekeeping is important to good personal hygiene. When your workroom and equipment are kept clean, there is little opportunity for accidental skin contact with corrosive chemicals, irritants or sensitizers. This is especially important because your hands are often wet. Keep the outside of bottles and other containers clean so chemicals won't get on your hands when you pick them up.

Keep your skin soft and clean. Do everything you can to avoid cuts, abrasions, chapping and cracking. When your skin is normal, it is harder for corrosive chemicals, irritants and sensitizers to affect it. When your hands are wet or have to be washed frequently, apply a good skin cream several times during the day to prevent them from becoming dry or chapped. Avoid harsh, abrasive soaps.

Wear rubber or neoprene gloves whenever there is danger of getting chemicals on your skin. This applies not only to corrosive and irritating chemicals, but also to deep-etch coating solution, deep-etch developer, deep-etching solution, copper-izing solution, alcohol wash, and plate etches. Contact with coating solution and plate etches that contain bichromate should especially be avoided. Wear neoprene gloves when you handle petroleum solvents or turpentine since these attack rubber. The proper care of protective gloves is very important. If they are not clean inside, they are worse than no gloves at all. The following precautions should therefore be taken:

1. Wash your gloves inside and outside each time you use them, and be sure your hands are clean when you put them on.
2. Be sure your gloves are free from cracks or leaks.
3. When you are wearing gloves, don't touch other parts of your body with them. Also, don't contaminate bottles or equipment you may later have to touch with your bare hands.

Should you get chemicals on your skin, especially ammonium bichromate and solutions that contain it, wash them immediately and thoroughly. Wash your hands and face before eating and at the end of your work day. Don't bring food, or eat it, in an area where contamination by chemicals might occur.

In case you should accidentally splash a chemical in your eyes, wash them quickly and thoroughly with water. An "eye cup" should be on hand for this purpose. Then consult a physisian, preferably an eye specialist, if your eyes remain irritated or inflamed. Don't use "eye drops" unless prescribed by your physician.

Take the precaution of wearing safety goggles whenever you handle strong acids or alkalies (lye) and there is any danger of splashing.

If you should develop dermatitis (itchy rash on hands or arms) consult a dermatologist (skin specialist). And if he establishes the fact that you have an allergy to certain materials like bichromate or turpentine, do everything you can to avoid contact with the materials. LTF has done a great deal of work to eliminate the use of skin sensitizers in lithography. As a result, there are now good non-bichromate plate etches, and the solvent called Lithotine that takes the place of turpentine.

For further information on personal hygiene in platemaking, you should read the following bulletins:

Chemical Safety Data Sheet SD-45, "Ammonium Bichromate", published by the Manufacturing Chemists' Association, Inc., 246 Woodward Building, 15th and H Streets, Washington 5, D. C.

LTF Technical Bulletin No. 6. "Prevention of Chemical Dermatitis in Lithography."

OPERATING PLATEMAKING EQUIPMENT

You may already be acquainted with the following safety procedures in using equipment such as carbon arc lamps, vacuum printing frames, whirlers, and fans. However, read them and add to them if your experience indicates that additional precautions are necessary.

Carbon arc lamps

Changing carbons:

1. Shut off current. Lock out and tag switch.
2. Wear heat resistant gloves and use pliers when removing hot carbons. Do not remove with bare hands.
3. Place used carbons in self-closing metal container to avoid possibility of fire. Do not throw on floor as they would also be a slipping or falling hazard.
4. Make sure everyone is in the clear before turning power on again.

Using carbon arc lamps:

1. Keep casters lubricated on portable units to avoid strains when moving arc lamps around.
2. Do not move arc lamps while they are burning.
3. Avoid striking steel or metal with arc lamp as it may short and cause a flash.
4. If arc lamp is located near whirler, do not touch arc lamp and whirler while arc lamp is on. It could give you a serious shock. Both pieces of equipment should be grounded.
5. Avoid tripping hazards by using drop cords rather than floor cords.
6. If floor is wooden, keep metal plate under arc lamps to catch hot carbon ash.
7. Use carbon ash catchers and clean these frequently.
8. Do not look directly into arc lights unless you are wear-

ing welder's goggles. The light from the carbon arc is strong in ultra-violet rays and can damage eyesight.

9. Do not use arc lamps as heat lamps for the body as serious burns may result very quickly.

10. Avoid inhaling fumes from carbon arc lamps.

Vacuum Printing Frames

1. Do not climb on bed of vacuum frames.

2. Keep vacuum frame closed when not in use.

3. Check springs of vacuum frame cover. Replace if necessary.

4. Make sure spring-operated frames are securely locked in position when being used.

5. Do not leave any objects on bed of vacuum frame.

6. Watch finger clearance when handling plates in and out of frame.

7. Keep fingers clear of clamping devices on vacuum frame.

8. Observe safety precautions pertaining to carbon arc lamps when these are used at vacuum printing frames.

Whirlers

1. Shut power off and lock out switch before working on whirler or when greasing it.

2. Do not use hands to stop whirler. You may break or cut your fingers.

3. Avoid undue strain or the possibility of falling into large whirler when bringing plates to the machine. If the whirler is difficult to reach, use a portable step, well marked and covered with a non-skid material.

4. Keep floor in front of whirler dry to avoid slipping or falling hazards, especially when bringing plates to the machine.

5. When coating plate in large whirler, keep your balance by using one hand on tub to support yourself.

6. In positioning plate, make sure plate is clamped securely to table so that it will not get loose and fly off. If whirler is the vertical type using four clamps, make sure all four clamps are securely fastened.

7. In positioning or handling the plate, watch out for rough or sharp edges which may cause cuts.

8. Do not leave tools or other objects in whirler.

9. If whirler has apron on it, be sure apron is locked in position before coating plate.

10. Keep doors of whirler closed. This is not only a safety feature but is a quality factor in getting dust-free coatings.

11. Keep whirlers clean. Do not clean them, however, when the power is on.

12. Do not start whirlers at high speed. Build speed up gradually.

13. Avoid contact with heating elements in unit. Heating elements should be grounded.

14. Keep water away from heating elements to avoid possibility of shock.

15. Keep drains of whirlers open. Clogging may cause water to back up and overflow.

16. Keep guard in place over belt of motor.

17. Lock out switch at end of shift so that the whirler cannot be started accidentally.

Fans

Portable fans are familiar pieces of equipment in deep-etch platemaking departments. Throughout this book reference is made to their use for drying purposes. For safety around fans the following precautions should be observed:

1. Do not attempt to twist or move electric fans around when they are still in motion.

2. Make sure portable fans are fastened securely so that they won't fall off tables or shelves due to vibration.

3. Avoid contact with fan blades. Regular guards supplied with some fans have rather large openings which are insufficient protection against fingers or hands which may come near the fan blades. Rubber blades substituted for the metal ones reduce injury possibilities. So does the addition of a substantial wire mesh screen, such as hardware cloth. At any rate, do not remove guards from fans. They have been put there for your protection.

APPENDIX

THE PREPARATION OF DEEP-ETCH CHEMICALS

When the gum deep-etch process was in its infancy, most shops prepared their own chemicals. Their formulas varied widely since little systematic research had been done. Considerable standardization took place, however, after LTF published formulas in 1934 based on its research.

The manufacture and sale of prepared deep-etch chemicals by suppliers took place gradually. As these were improved, their acceptance by the trade increased. Recent surveys show that the majority of shops now use commercial, prepared deep-etch chemicals. For the benefit of shops that prefer to prepare their own chemicals, the following formulas and instructions are given.

For descriptions of the various materials used in platemaking chemicals, and the precautions necessary to avoid possible harmful effects in handling them, see Chapter 3.

Counter-Etches for Zinc and Stainless Steel Plates

	Metric Units	U. S. Units
Hydrochloric Acid (HCl), 37.0-38.5%	8 cc.	1 liq. oz. (30 cc.)
Water	1000 cc.	1 gallon
or		
Acetic Acid ($HC_2H_3O_2$), 99%	50 cc.	6 liq. oz. (178 cc.)
Water	1000 cc.	1 gallon

Either counter-etch can be used.

Counter-Etch for Aluminum Plates

	Metric Units	U. S. Units
Acetic Acid ($HC_2H_3O_2$), 99%	50 cc.	6 liq. oz. (178 cc.)
Water	1000 cc.	1 gallon

Cronak Solution for Zinc Plates

	Metric Units	U. S. Units
Ammonium Bichromate [(NH₄)₂Cr₂O₇]	360 g.	12 avoir. oz. (350 g.)
Water	20 liters	5 gallons
Sulfuric Acid (H₂SO₄) Conc., Sp. Gr. 1.84	63 cc.	2 liq. oz. (59 cc.)

Dissolve the ammonium bichromate in the water first, then add the sulfuric acid slowly while stirring the solution. Adding the sulfuric acid last, with stirring, is very important. Never add water to the strong sulfuric acid as this might cause an explosion and injure you. For other precautions in making and handling the Cronak solution, review Chapter 3, page 24. The pH value of the finished Cronak solution should be between 1.4 and 1.7.

Brunak Solution for Aluminum Plates

	Metric Units	U. S. Units
Ammonium Bichromate [(NH₄)₂Cr₂O₇]	1350 g.	45 avoir. oz.
Water	20 liters	5 gallons
Hydrofluoric Acid (HF), 48%	160 cc.	5 liq. oz. (150 cc.)

Since Brunak solution contains hydrofluoric acid, it should not be kept in glass, stoneware or galvanized iron vessels unless they are lined with acid-proof material. The best containers to use are one-gallon polyethylene bottles.

Deep-Etch Coating Solution

	Metric Units	U. S. Units
Gum Arabic Solution, 14° Bé	720 cc.	3 quarts
Ammonium Bichromate Stock Solution	240 cc.	1 quart
Ammonium Hydroxide, 28% NH₃	36 cc.	4¾ liq. oz. (140 cc.)

Mix the gum solution and the ammonium bichromate stock solution thoroughly, then add the ammonia. (Mix carefully so as not to beat air into the solution in fine bubbles.) Strain through six or eight thicknesses of damp cheesecloth. If made correctly, the coating solution will test between 14.0° and 14.2° Baumé at 77° F. (25° C.). Its pH value will be 8.8 to 9.0. The higher the pH, the longer will be the shelf life of the solution.

Ammonium Bichromate Stock Solution

	Metric Units	U. S. Units
Ammonium Bichromate [(NH₄)₂Cr₂O₇], Photo Grade	200 g.	26¾ avoir. oz. (758 g.)
Water to make	1000 cc.	1 gallon

Dissolve the ammonium bichromate in about three-fourths of the water. Then add water to make up to the final volume. The finished stock solution should test 14.2° Baumé at 77° F. (25° C.).

14° Baumé Gum Arabic Solution

	Metric Units	U. S. Units
Gum Arabic, Select Sorts	284 g.	36 avoir. oz.
Water	714 cc.	92 liq. oz.
Carbolic Acid (Phenol)	2.0 cc.	¼ liq. oz. (7.5 cc.)

To prevent souring, add the carbolic acid to the water first. Then dissolve the gum arabic. Test the solution with a hydrometer and adjust it to 14° Baumé by adding small quantities of water, mixing thoroughly each time before testing. The temperature should be between 75° and 79° F. to give the right Baumé reading.

Other preservatives than carbolic acid can be used. These include sodium benzoate, sodium salicylate, methylhydroxybenzoate, the Dowicides, and the Santicides. All are effective. Carbolic acid is recommended because it is easy to obtain, easy to handle, and is good enough for the purpose.

CAUTION: Never use mercuric chloride or any other mercury salt to preserve gum arabic solutions that will be used on aluminum plates. The slightest trace of a mercury salt will cause corrosion pitting of aluminum and produce "ink-dot scum", (see page 48).

METHODS OF DISSOLVING GUM ARABIC

To dissolve gum arabic, you can use one of the following methods:

1. Place gum sorts in a bag made of cheesecloth, muslin, or flannel. If you use cheesecloth, use six or eight thicknesses. Suspend the bag in the water so that half or two-thirds of the gum is submerged, and allow to stand overnight. Then lift the bag out of the solution and let it drain. *Do not squeeze the bag.*

2. Add gum sorts to the water in a stoneware jar and stir occasionally by hand until the gum is all dissolved. This usually takes about 24 hours. Then strain the solution through several thicknesses of damp cheesecloth to remove dirt and woody material.

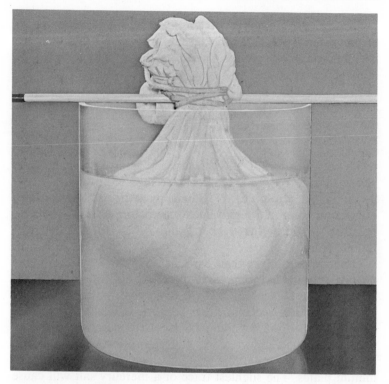

Figure 70. Dissolving gum arabic sorts by the bag method gives the cleanest, clearest solution.

3. Add powdered gum arabic to the water with constant stirring. A low-speed mechanical stirrer helps. This method takes less time, but the solution contains dirt that cannot be strained out with cheesecloth. It takes a pressure filter to give a clean, clear solution from powdered gum arabic.

Of these methods, No. 1 is preferred since it gives the cleanest, clearest solutions, most suitable for deep-etch coating. If you use this method, no special filtering equipment is needed.

In making gum solution for the deep-etch coating, avoid violent stirring or beating air into the solution. Fine air bubbles take a long time to rise. Often you cannot see them until you coat a plate. When the coating dries, the bubbles break and leave pinholes.

TESTING GUM ARABIC

Stringy or "ropy" gum has always been a source of trouble. It is caused by part of the gum failing to dissolve properly. Some lots of gum arabic contain lumps that simply swell to a soft gelatinous mass that is broken up and dispersed by the stirring. At first the solution appears to be all right but, on standing, it becomes stringy or gelatinous. Such unsatisfactory gum arabic can be detected by the following tests:

Figure 71. This is how gum arabic sorts can be tested for the presence of undesirable gelatinous gum.

For Gum Arabic Sorts (lumps)

Place a single layer of lumps of gum sorts in a flat dish or tray and add enough water to about half submerge them. Cover the dish or tray and let stand overnight. Then, if all the lumps have dissolved or "melted", the gum is satisfactory. If, however, some of the lumps have simply swollen and become gelatinous, the gum should be rejected.

For Powdered or Granulated Gum Arabic

Dissolve 30 grams of the gum in 70 cc. of water and let stand overnight. Test by pouring slowly from one vessel to another. Good gum will form a smooth syrup. If there is any lumpiness or ropiness, the gum is not suitable for deep-etch coatings.

Gum arabic that makes stringy or ropy solutions will sometimes improve with age. It has been found that, if the dry gum is stored for six months or longer, it will "mellow". Often, after such aging, it will make satisfactory coating solutions.

KEEPING QUALITIES OF THE COATING SOLUTION

Experience has shown no advantage in keeping the prepared deep-etch coating solution in a refrigerator. In fact, studies at the LTF laboratory indicate that this practice is a source of coating trouble. Solutions kept cold have a greater tendency to produce uneven, streaked coatings. Air bubbles remain in suspension and do not separate. It is recommended, therefore, that you keep your coating solution at room temperature. The ammonia in it acts as a stabilizer, and at pH 8.8 to 9.0 it will usually keep for several months. However, different lots of gum have different keeping qualities, and it is usually not advisable to stock coating solution more than three months ahead.

WETTING AGENTS

The idea of adding a wetting agent to the deep-etch coating solution to improve its coating properties has occurred to many platemakers. The problem is to find one that works well and consistently. Some wetting agents coagulate gum arabic. Others work well with one batch of gum but not with others. No systematic search has been made for the best material since there are hundreds of wetting agents.

A good coating solution, free from air bubbles and gelatinous matter, will produce a good coating provided the plate is clean. If it does not, the plate has not been counter-etched properly. A wetting agent can only make the coating cover the traces of grease or dirt on the plate and make the coating look good, when in reality it is not. LTF recommends careful counter-etching, in which case no wetting agent has been found necessary.

DYE FOR COATINGS

Many platemakers like a dyed coating since the plate image shows a little more contrast when developed. The deep-etch coating solution (Formula No. 3) can be dyed by adding 7.5 cc. of dye solution to a liter, or one ounce of dye solution to a gallon. The dye solution is made as follows:

Dye Solution for Deep-Etch Coating

	Metric Units	U. S. Units
Blue Dye*	28.5 g.	1 avoir. oz. (28.5 g.)
Distilled Water	340 cc.	12 liq. oz.

*Probably the best blue dye for deep-etch coatings is Color Index No. 671. It is sold under the following names:
Alphazurine FGND Conc., National Aniline Div., Allied Chemical and Dye Corporation
Amacid Blue FG, Conc., American Aniline Products, Inc.
Calcocid Blue EG, Calco Chemical Div., American Cyanamid Company
Kiton Pure Blue LN, Ciba Company, Inc.
Neptune Blue BRA, Conc., General Dyestuff Corporation

Dissolve the dye and allow the solution to settle overnight. Then, without stirring up any sediment, strain it through coarse filter paper.

Dye doesn't appear to change the coating sensitivity. However, it does mask any color changes in the coating solution due to aging.

COMMERCIAL DEEP-ETCH COATING SOLUTIONS

Prepared deep-etch coating solutions can be purchased from a number of litho supply houses, together with developers, deep-etching solutions, lacquers, developing inks, and other preparations. In general, these commercial coating solutions are like the one given here; they are mostly bichromated gum arabic solutions containing ammonia. There are, however, slight differences and the preparations sold with them are adjusted accordingly. It is recommended, therefore, that if you select a commercial coating, you use the developer and deep-etching solution that go with it. Don't try to use A's coating solution with B's developer and C's deep-etching acid.

Stopping-Out Shellac

	Metric Units	U. S. Units
Orange Shellac	250 g.	8 avoir. oz. (227 g.)
Denatured Alcohol, Water-Free	1000 cc.	1 quart
Methyl Violet Dye	2 g.	$\frac{1}{16}$ avoir. oz. (2 g.)

The water-free denatured alcohol can be Ansol M, Anhydrous Solox, Anhydrous Synacol, or Shellacol (see page 119).

There are also a number of commercial stop-out lacquers that work as well as shellac. These flow well from the brush and, being soluble in alcohol, are removed by the alcohol wash. Regular deep-etch lacquers generally do not work. They are not designed for application with a brush, and most of them don't dissolve in alcohol.

Regular Deep-Etch Developer

	Metric Units	U. S. Units
Calcium Chloride Solution, 40-41° Bé	1000 cc.	1 gallon
Lactic Acid, 85%	53 cc.	6¾ liq. oz. (200 cc.)

To make the calcium chloride solution, dissolve 9½ pounds of commercial calcium chloride ($CaCl_2.2H_2O$) in one gallon of water. Allow the solution to cool to room temperature and adjust its Baumé to 40-41° by adding water. Let it settle and pour off the clear liquor. Strain through cheesecloth to remove dirt.

Stabilized Deep-Etch Developer

	Metric Units	U. S. Units
Water	1000 cc.	2 quarts
Zinc Chloride (ZnCl$_2$), Technical	350 g.	1½ pounds
Calcium Chloride (CaCl$_2$ · 2H$_2$O),		
Commercial	700 g.	3 pounds
Lactic Acid, 85%	160 cc.	11½ liq. oz. (340 cc.)

Dissolve the materials in the order in which they are listed. When dissolved, add water until the hydrometer reads 41.4-41.5° Baumé at 78-80° F. Make this solution carefully. Its Baumé must be exactly as specified.

Zinc Deep-Etching Solution

	Metric Units	U. S. Units
Calcium Chloride Solution, 40-41° Bé	1000 cc.	1 gallon
Iron Perchloride, Lumps	25 g.	3¼ avoir. oz. (92 g.)
Hydrochloric Acid, C.P., 37-38.5%	20 cc,	2½ liq. oz. (74 cc.)

Use the same calcium chloride solution as for the Regular Developer above. The finished deep-etching solution should test 40-41° Baumé at 77° F.

Aluminum Deep-Etching Solution

	Metric Units	U. S. Units
Calcium Chloride Solution, 40-41° Bé	1000 cc.	89 liq. oz.
Zinc Chloride (ZnCl$_2$), Technical	380 g.	35½ avoir. oz.
Iron Perchloride Solution, 50-51° Bé	285 cc.	25¼ liq. oz.
Hydrochloric Acid (HCl), 37-38.5%	114 cc.	1¼ liq. oz. (37 cc.)
Cupric Chloride (CuCl$_2$ · 2H$_2$O)	27 g.	2½ avoir. oz. (70 g.)

Use the same calcium chloride solution as for the Regular Deep-Etch Developer. The finished solution should have a density of 50-52° Baumé at 77° F. (25° C.).

The 50-51° Baumé Iron Perchloride Solution

	Metric Units	U. S. Units
Iron Perchloride (FeCl$_3$), Lumps,		
Technical Anhydrous	1080 g.	9 pounds
Water	1000 cc.	1 gallon
or		
Iron Perchloride, Crystals (FeCl$_3$ · 6H$_2$O)	4800 g.	10 pounds
Water	1000 cc.	1 quart

Dissolve the iron perchloride in the water in an earthenware crock. To make it dissolve rapidly, use hot water. Cool the finished solution to 77° F. (25° C.) and adjust its Baumé to 50-51° by adding water or iron perchloride, whichever is required.

If the deep-etching solution seems to work too fast, cut down the amount of cupric chloride in the formula to 2 or even 1½ ounces.

Nicohol Solution

	Metric Units	U.S. Units
Cellosolve Solvent	900 cc.	3 quarts
Nitric Acid (HNO$_3$) Conc., Sp. Gr. 1.42	100 cc.	10 liq. oz.

Add the nitric acid to the Cellosolve Solvent slowly, with constant stirring. Never add the solvent to the acid since the reaction might be explosive and spatter acid on you. While nitric acid is extremely corrosive in water solution, the Nicohol mixture is relatively harmless. If it gets on your skin, simply wash it off with water.

Copperizing Solution

	Metric Units	U. S. Units
Isopropyl Alcohol, 99%	1000 cc.	1 quart
Cuprous Chloride (Cu$_2$Cl$_2$)	31 g.	1 avoir. oz. (28.3 g.)
Hydrochloric Acid, 37.0-38.5%	32 cc.	1 liq. oz. (29.6 cc.)

Add the powdered cuprous chloride to the isopropyl alcohol while stirring, then add the hydrochloric acid and continue stirring until dissolved. If the cuprous chloride is lumpy, place the amount needed on a glass plate or stone and break up the lumps by rubbing with a spatula. Lumpy cuprous chloride dissolves very slowly.

Phosphate Solution for Zinc Plates

	Metric Units	U. S. Units
Aluminum Sulfate [Al$_2$(SO$_4$)$_3$ · 18H$_2$O]	15.1 g.	2 avoir. oz. (57 g.)
Potassium Nitrate (KNO$_3$)	11.5 g.	1½ avoir. oz. (42 g.)
Ammonium Phosphate, Monobasic (NH$_4$H$_2$PO$_4$)	21 g.	2¾ avoir. oz. (78 g.)
Water	1000 cc.	1 gallon

Dissolve the aluminum sulfate and potassium nitrate in half of the water. Dissolve the ammonium phosphate in the other half. Mix the two solutions to make the Phosphate solution.

The finished solution should have a pH value between 2.4 and 2.6.

When the Phosphate solution stands for awhile, it tends to form a precipitate of aluminum phosphate ($AlPO_4$). This settles to the bottom of the vessel and forms a hard cake, but it doesn't affect the way the solution works. You need only be careful not to let any of the hard material get on the plate and scratch its surface.

You can avoid this hard precipitate by keeping the two solutions separate and mixing equal amounts of them to form fresh Phosphate solution each time you need it. Before they are mixed these solutions will keep indefinitely.

Nital Solution for Zinc Plates

	Metric Units	U. S. Units
Ammonium Alum,		
[$NH_4Al(SO_4)_2 \cdot 12H_2O$]	30 g.	4 avoir. oz. (113 g.)
Nitric Acid (HNO_3), Conc.,		
Sp. Gr. 1.42	1 cc.	⅛ liq. oz. (3.7 cc.)
Water	1000 cc.	1 gallon

The small amount of nitric acid is all that is needed with tap waters of medium hardness. It gives the solution a pH value of 2.4 to 2.6. With waters of very low or very high hardness, you may have to decrease or increase the amount of nitric acid.

Precaution: Don't substitute potassium alum for the ammonium alum. This would not give good desensitization.

Cellulose Gum Plate Etch for Zinc Plates

	Metric Units	U. S. Units
Water	750 cc.	3 quarts
Phosphoric Acid (H_3PO_4), 85%	7.8 cc	1 liq. oz. (29.5 cc.)
Magnesium Nitrate, Crystals		
[$Mg(NO_3)_2 \cdot 6H_2O$]	11.3 g.	1½ avoir. oz. (42.5 g.)
Cellulose Gum, Dry	41 g.	5½ avoir. oz. (156 g.)
Water to make	1000 cc.	1 gallon

Dissolve the materials in the order given.

When you come to the cellulose gum, add it slowly, stirring continously to prevent lumping. After it is all in, stir occasionally for about two hours or until the gum is dissolved. You can use warm or even hot water to make it dissolve faster. When it is all dissolved, add water to make up the final volume. The finished etch should test between 2.9 and 3.3 pH.

In the United States, cellulose gum can be bought from the Hercules Powder Co., Wilmington, Delaware, and from a number of litho supply houses. Ask for "CMC 70-LL for Lithographic Use". In other countries the trade names and manufacturers are:

Canada: *Low Viscosity Carboxel,* Standard Chemical Company, Toronto.

England: *Cellofas WFZ,* Imperial Chemical Industries, London.

Sweden: *Cellufix FF Low,* Swedish Cellulose Corporation, Stockholm.

Tannic-Alum Etch for Zinc Plates, Formula No. 1

	Metric Units	U. S. Units
Water	320 cc.	40 liq. oz.
Tannic Acid	20.6 g.	2¾ avoir. oz. (78 g.)
Chrome Alum [KCr(SO$_4$)$_2 \cdot$ 12H$_2$O]	30 g.	4 avoir oz. (113 g.)
Phosphoric Acid (H$_3$PO$_4$), 85%	21.4 cc.	2¾ liq. oz. (81 cc.)
Gum Arabic Solution, 14° Bé	680 cc.	88 liq. oz.

Dissolve the tannic acid in the water first. Then add the chrome alum and stir till completely dissolved before adding the phosphoric acid. Finally, add the gum arabic solution and mix thoroughly. The finished etch should have a pH value of 1.8 to 2.0.

Gum-Bichromate Etch for Zinc Plates, Formula No. 2

	Metric Units	U. S. Units
Water	30 cc.	4 liq. oz. (118 cc.)
Ammonium Bichromate [(NH$_4$)$_2$Cr$_2$O$_7$], C.P. or Photo Grade	7.5 g.	1 avoir. oz. (28.3 g.)
Gum Arabic Solution, 12-14° Bé	945 cc.	121 liq. oz.
Phosphoric Acid (H$_3$PO$_4$), 85%	18.5 cc.	2⅜ liq. oz. (70 cc.)

Dissolve the ammonium bichromate in the water. Add this solution to the gum arabic solution and mix thoroughly. Finally, add the phosphoric acid and again mix thoroughly. The finished etch should test between 2.0 and 2.5 pH.

Plate Etch for Aluminum and Stainless Steel Plates

	Metric Units	U. S. Units
Gum Arabic Solution, 12-14° Bé	1000 cc.	1 gallon
Phosphoric Acid (H$_3$PO$_4$), 85%	31 cc.	4 liq. oz. (118 cc.)

Simply add the phosphoric acid to the gum solution and mix thoroughly. This etch should have a pH value of 1.9 to 2.1.

Lithotine

	Metric Units	U. S. Units
Pine Oil, Water-free	90 cc.	10 liq. oz. (296 cc.)
Castor Oil, Technical	9 cc.	1 liq. oz. (30 cc.)
Ester Gum, powdered	18 g.	2 avoir. oz. (57 g.)
V.M.&P. Naphtha or Dry Cleaners Naphtha	1000 cc.	7 pints

There are two ways to prepare Lithotine: (1) Mix the pine oil, castor oil and ester gum, heat the mixture until the ester gum is dissolved, cool and add the naphtha; (2) put all four ingredients in a container and shake or stir, without heat, until the ester gum is dissolved.

Asphaltum Solution

	Metric Units	U. S. Units
Powdered Asphaltum or Gilsonite, (turpentine soluble)	175 g.	23 avoir. oz. (650 g.)
Lithotine	1000 cc.	1 gallon

Stir the mixture until the asphaltum is dissolved and strain the solution through muslin or a similar cloth of fairly fine weave.

Lithotine is preferable to turpentine since it is less irritant to the skin and less likely to cause dermatitis (see Chapter 3, page 34).

Chromium Etch for Bimetal Plates

	Metric Units	U. S. Units
Aluminum Chloride ($AlCl_3$) Solution, 32° Bé	750 cc.	3 quarts
Zinc Chloride ($ZnCl_2$), Technical	630 g.	5¼ lbs.
Phosphoric Acid (H_3PO_4), 85%	40 cc.	5 liq. oz.

The 32° Baumé aluminum chloride solution can be made from anhydrous (water-free) aluminum chloride ($AlCl_3$) by dissolving about 540 grams in 1000 cc. of water, or 4½ pounds in a gallon of water. But if you start with crystalline aluminum chloride ($AlCl_3.6H_2O$), you would have to dissolve 1750 grams in 1000 cc. of water, or 14½ pounds in a gallon of water.

To make the chromium etch, dissolve the zinc chloride in the 32° Bé aluminum chloride solution. This should bring the Baumé up to 55°. If it doesn't, add more zinc chloride. Finally, add the phosphoric acid.

Special Counter-Etch for Adding Tusche Work on Aluminum and Stainless Steel Plates

	Metric Units	U. S. Units
Ammonium Alum		
$NH_4Al(SO_4)_2 \cdot 12H_2O$	7.5 g.	1 avoir. oz. (28 g.)
Hydrofluoric Acid (HF), 48%	7.8 cc.	1 liq. oz. (29 cc.)
Water to make	1000 cc.	1 gallon

Dissolve the ammonium alum in part of the water and add the hydrofluoric acid. Then make up to the final volume with water.

INDEX

220

Foundation Publications